Handbook of
ACOUSTICAL
ENCLOSURES
and BARRIERS

by Richard K. Miller
and Wayne V. Montone

PUBLISHERS OF TECHNICAL AND SAFETY BOOKS

THE FAIRMONT PRESS, INC.

134 PEACHTREE STREET, SUITE 918 • ATLANTA, GEORGIA 30303 • (404) 876-1113

Contents

Handbook of
Acoustical Enclosures
and Barriers

1

The Role of Enclosures in Industry

More acoustical enclosures are employed to solve industrial noise problems than any other single measure. When it is recognized that the cost estimate for industries in the United States to reduce sound levels to 90 dBA is 10.5 billion dollars, both the dollar value and environmental importance associated with the proper design of these structures can be appreciated.

Acoustical enclosures provide the greatest noise reduction potential of all approaches which may be taken to equipment noise abatement. Noise reductions of 20-30 dBA are common with machine enclosures, and with special isolation treatment, noise reductions above 50 dBA may be achieved. An acoustical enclosure installed in Tennessee reduced the 136 dBA sound levels associated with the testing of sirens to below the outdoor ambient sound level of 28 dBA: a noise reduction of over 100 dBA!

The size of enclosures may vary by a ratio of several billion to one! In Florida, an acoustical enclosure was proposed to encompass an entire electrical power generating plant. The smallest acoustical enclosure on record is a unit installed on an ultrasonic welding head in Indiana, with a total volume of less than 1½ cubic inches. The largest movable acoustical wall system in the world, which was designed by Industrial Acoustic Company, towers 42 feet at the Kansas City Convention Center. An acoustical enclosure accompanied our astronauts on a trip to the moon as part of a silencing package on an air moving system. The installation of acoustical enclosures even played an integral role in resolving a recent strike by employees in an Illinois metal stamping plant.

MOTIVES FOR REDUCING NOISE

American industry has three motives to reduce workplace sound levels:

1. To prevent hearing loss
2. To insure a pleasant working environment for employees
3. To comply with OSHA regulations

HEARING LOSS

It is estimated that between 8.7 and 11.1 million Americans suffered a permanent hearing disability.[1] The quality of life of these individuals is generally significantly degraded because of their reduced ability to carry out communications in their business and personal lives. It is well established that prolonged exposure to excessive noise levels will result in a permanent hearing loss. The probability of incurring a hearing loss greater than 25 dB ranges from 18% for exposure to 90 dBA to 70% for exposure to 115 dBA for a working lifetime of 40 years.[2] An industry is held responsible for hearing loss incurred by employees which is attributable to noise exposure associated with their jobs, and is legally liable to compensate employees when hearing loss is identified. With 75% of the nation's workforce exposed to sound levels above 85 dBA, potential worker's compensation liability for hearing loss has been estimated to be on the order of $12 billion.

A 1976 survey by Dr. Meyer S. Fox reported that Workmen's Compensation awards of more than $25,000 for hearing loss are possible in 20% of 50 states. The range of possible awards is from $9,000 to $109,000, averaging $14,000 to $15,000, and between 180 and 185 weeks of pay.[3]

ENVIRONMENT OF THE WORKPLACE

The concern for worker welfare extends beyond the risk of hearing damage to other physiological and psychological effects, including annoyance. It is simply unpleasant to work in a noisy environment. Studies have indicated that workers are both less happy and less productive in areas of high ambient noise when compared to similar jobs in quieter workplaces. A recent NIOSH study showed that the increase in overall absenteeism among workers in noisy areas as compared with non-noisy areas is on the order of 1.23 workers per hundred per day. At a $4.50 basic wage, this represents an average of $115 per worker per year.

OSHA REGULATION

Title 29 CFR, Section 1910.95 of the Williams-Steiger Occupational Safety and Health Act of 1970 (Public Law 91-596) pertains to the protection of workers from potentially hazardous occupational noise. The regulation established a maximum noise level of 90 dBA for a continuous 8-hour exposure during a working day. Higher sound levels are allowed for shorter exposure times. The Occupational Safety and Health Administration (OSHA) of the U.S. Department of Labor was created for the purpose of implementing and enforcing the law.

Enforcement of the noise standard shows an increasing trend, with 43% of the 10,641 noise samples by OSHA compliance officers between January 1973 and March 1975 resulting in proposed penalties of $169,042. An economic impact study recently published by OSHA concluded that industry would have to spend $10.5 billion to comply with engineering requirements for a 90 dBA standard.

ENVIRONMENTAL NOISE

The national concern for the wide-spread adverse effects of environmental noise has also created a demand for the development of noise control programs. The foremost complaint of Americans about their neighborhoods is noise, according to a Census Bureau study released on 24 May 1976. The Bureau said its annual housing survey showed 49.2 per cent of American households feel their neighborhoods are too noisy. By contrast, only about a third as many—12.1 million compared to 34.9 million—feel crime in their neighborhoods is high enough to be considered an undesirable condition. The noise complaints were largest by proportion—64.8 per cent—in central cities. They were smallest—43.2 per cent—outside of metropolitan areas.

BACKGROUND

With the emphasis on noise control and an abundance of technical information available on the subject which has been available for several years, the authors have recognized that most readers of this book are familiar with the fundamentals of acoustics. As a brief refresher, a complete glossary of noise control terminology is presented at the end of this book.

BOOK ORGANIZATION

The following chapters of this book are designed to provide the engineer with complete information to design or specify an acoustical enclosure system.

Chapter 2 describes the rating systems used to define the properties of sound abosrptive materials and the testing methods used.

Design solutions are outlined in Chapter 3 for special requirements of acoustical systems: protection from damage and contaminant abuse, fire codes, FDA and USDA requirements, and high-temperature environments.

Chapter 4 summarizes the engineering equations relating to wall design, and describes the parameters relating to the effectiveness of double walls and composite walls. These wall design analyses form the basis for both employee and machine enclosures. A method for estimating sound transmission loss is presented.

Employee enclosure design parameters are presented in Chapter 5, and design features related to location, size, visibility, accessibility, comfort, safety, and productivity are discussed.

Chapter 6 describes analysis and design procedures for machine enclosures. Practical aspects of enclosure design related to productivity, fire prevention, safety, the effect of openings, and feasibility are covered.

An unusual type of machine enclosure which involves direct treatment of noise producing machine elements is described in Chapter 7. Design procedures, sketches, and a list of thirty-five typical applications are presented.

Reducing machine heat build-up and providing cooling and ventilation for employees are the most important nonacoustical design requirements related to enclosure design. Complete design analysis procedures are presented in Chapter 8 to insure proper design of ventilation and cooling systems.

Chapter 9 outlines design guidelines for in-plant barriers, and shows how to avoid barrier ineffectiveness in reverberant sound fields.

A cost-benefit analysis is an important aspect of any noise control program. Chapter 10 presents guidelines for economic assessment of enclosure systems: material and installation costs, production influences, energy considerations, and economic benefits.

Examples of commercially available acoustical enclosure and barrier systems are presented in Chapter 11.

Chapter 12 contains data tables of material properties, sound transmission losses, and absorption coefficients.

REFERENCES

1. "Report to the President and Congress on Noise," Administrator to the Environmental Protection Agency, 92nd Congress Document No. 92-63, February 1972.
2. "Impact of Noise Control at the Workplace," Bolt, Beranek and Newman Report No. 2671, October 29, 1973.
3. *Noise Regulation Reporter,* Number 63, 11 October 1976.

2

Acoustical Material Rating Systems

The proper approach to the design of acoustical enclosures involves calculation of expected noise reduction values. An enclosure system which is underdesigned may result in an unnecessarily loud work environment and possible legal violations and associated monetary penalties. Overdesigned systems may be unnecessarily costly.

The engineering principles relating to the noise attenuation of enclosures and barriers are well established. Guidelines for the performance of calculations for most basic design approaches are presented in this book. The assumptions behind these engineering equations would not be expected to lead to errors of a significant magnitude. For industrial situations without unusual circumstances, estimated noise reductions based on the equations of this book should not lead to significant errors (accuracies related to the assumptions beyond the equations should be in the ±3 dBA range). The overall accuracy associated with the application of barrier and enclosure equations is dependent upon the reliability of the acoustical data utilized in the calculations. In order to expect reliable results, it is imperative that accurate values related to the noise reduction properties of the acoustical materials be employed in the calculation. The basis for reliable testing of acoustical materials is presented in this chapter.

7

BASIC CLASSES OF MATERIALS

Two classes of materials are used for the construction of acoustical enclosures and barriers:

1. **sound barrier materials**—reduce sound transmission between adjacent spaces
2. **sound absorptive materials**—reduce reflected sound from surfaces and decrease reverberation

The quantity used to rate sound barriers is the sound transmission loss, abbreviated TL. Sound absorptive materials are rated by the sound absorption coefficient, designated by the small case Greek letter alpha, α.

Many engineering materials are rated under nonstandardized and varying conditions, rendering published performance data relatively useless to the investigator. Fortunately for the specifying engineer, performance ratings for sound barrier and absorptive materials have been standardized to allow presentation of recognized and valid data by material manufacturers. The standards of the American Society for Testing and Materials (ASTM), discussed in this chapter, are available from: American Society for Testing and Materials, 1916 Race Street, Philadelphia, PA 19103.

SOUND TRANSMISSION LOSS

The sound transmission loss of a partition in a specified frequency band is the ratio, expressed in decibels, of the airborne sound power incident on the partition to the sound power transmitted by the partition and radiated on the other side. The sound transmission loss is measured in the laboratory by measuring the sound pressure level difference in two rooms with the acoustical wall being tested installed between them. The transmission loss is given by the following equation:

$$TL = L_p(s) - L_p(r) + 10 \log \frac{S}{A} \qquad (2\text{-}1)$$

where: TL   = sound transmission loss, dB

$L_p(s)$ = sound pressure level in source room, dB re .0002 microbar

$L_p(r)$ = sound pressure level in receiving room, dB re .0002 microbar

S   = area of test wall, ft^2

A   = sound absorption in receiving room, Sabins

The test for transmission loss has been standardized as ASTM Standard E90-70 for the "Laboratory Measurement of Airborne Sound Transmission Loss of Building Partitions." The transmission loss may also be defined as 10 times the logarithm (base 10) of the incident sound energy on a wall to the sound transmitted through it, or:

$$TL = 10 \log_{10} \frac{w_i}{w_t} \qquad (2\text{-}2)$$

where: TL   = transmission loss, dB

w_i = incident sound energy, watts

w_t = transmitted sound energy, watts

TRANSMISSION COEFFICIENT

An alternate definition of the transmission loss involves the transmission coefficient, τ. The transmission coefficient is defined to be the fraction of the incident energy that is transmitted through a wall. The transmission loss may then be defined as 10 times the logarithm (base 10) of the reciprocal of the transmission coefficient, or

$$TL = 10 \log \frac{1}{\tau} \qquad (2\text{-}3)$$

where: TL   = sound transmission loss, dB

τ = transmission coefficient

NOISE REDUCTION COEFFICIENT

To provide a single number rating descriptor of sound absorptive materials, the Noise Reduction Coefficient, NRC, is used. The NRC is the average of the sound absorption coefficients at the four frequencies of 250, 500, 1000, and 2000 Hertz. In expressing the NRC, the value is rounded to the nearest multiple of 0.05.

STANDARD TRANSMISSION CLASS

The Sound Transmission Class, STC, as defined by ASTM Standard E413-70T, "Determination of Sound Transmission Class," is a single numerical average of a barrier's transmission loss performance and may be used for preliminary acoustical assessments. It is commonly used for speech and office noise situations. The broken line curve of Figure 2.1 which has three segments of different slopes, is called a sound transmission class contour.

The procedure generally used to establish the STC value for a material is to plot the one-third octave band sound transmission loss values, and to adjust a transparent overlay of the STC contour (traced from Figure 2.1) until the maximum STC value meeting the above criteria is obtained using the following rules:

1.   The maximum deviation of the test curve below the contour of any single test frequency shall not exceed 8 dB.

2.   The sum of the deviations at all the frequencies of the test curve below the contour shall not exceed 32 dB—an average deviation of 2 dB.

The curve intercept at 500 Hertz is taken as the STC value.

A sample plot used to determine the STC for ¾" plywood is shown in Figure 2.2.

Transmission loss data, usually presented as one-third octave band transmission loss values, may be converted into octave band TL values, using Figure 2.3. This conversion assumes equal

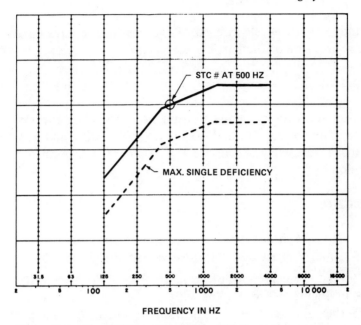

FREQUENCY IN HZ

Figure 2.1. Sound Transmission Class (STC) overlay contour.

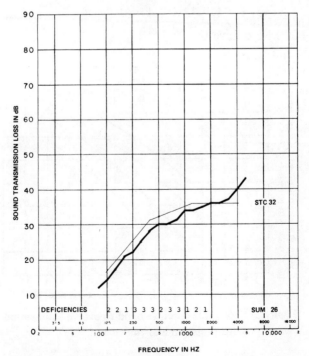

FREQUENCY IN HZ

Figure 2.2. Determination of STC value for ¾" plywood.[1]

sound pressure levels in each of the one-third octave bands on the source side of the barrier.

EXAMPLE

The one-third octave band transmission loss values for one-inch thick glass are 33, 36, and 40 for the 800, 1000, and 1250 Hz bands, respectively. Compute the 1000 Hz octave band transmission loss.

SOLUTION

Highest value—Lowest value = 40−36 = 7
Highest value—Lowest value = 40−36 = 4

First, project upward from the value 7 on the horizontal axis of Figure 2.3 to the line with the value 4. From the vertical axis, the value 2.4 is read. The value is added to the lowest TL value, or:

$$TL = 33 + 2.4 = 37.4 \text{ dB}$$

for the 1000 Hz octave band.

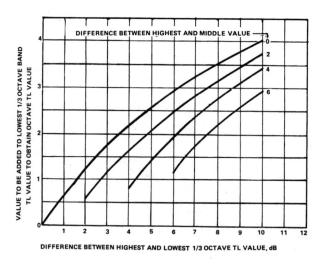

Figure 2.3. One-third octave band to octave band sound transmission loss conversion.[2]

ABSORPTION COEFFICIENT

The Sound Absorption Coefficient, α, used for rating sound absorptive materials describes the fraction of incident sound energy that an acoustical material absorbs. Two test procedures are outlined by the American Society for Testing and Materials to assign a value ranging of unity 1.0, total absorption, to 0, a totally reflective surface to describe a material's performance.

ASTM Standard C423-66 provides a "Standard Method of Test for Sound Absorption of Acoustical Materials in Reverberation Rooms" which uses a room with a reverberant (diffuse) sound field. This standard has been adapted by the American National Standards Institute as ANSI 1.7-1970. To determine the absorption coefficient, the decay time (the time a steady state sound requires to decrease by 60 dB) is measured before and after a specimen of 72 ft^2 is introduced into a reverberant room. The total sound absorption of the room, A, is given by the Sabine equation:

$$A = 0.9210 \frac{Vt}{C} \qquad (2\text{-}4)$$

where: A = total absorption in Sabins, ft^2

V = volume, ft^3

t = decay time, $\frac{dB}{sec}$

c = speed of sound, $\frac{ft}{sec}$

The absorption added by the specimen is derived by taking the difference of the two room absorption values:

$$A_s = A_2 - A_1 = 0.9210\,(t_2 - t_1)/C \qquad (2\text{-}5)$$

where: A_s = absorption due to specimen, Sabins, ft^2

A_2 = absorption of room with specimen, Sabins, ft^2

A_1 = absorption of room without specimen, Sabins, ft^2

t_2 = decay time with specimen, dB/sec

t_1 = decay time without specimen, dB/sec

The absorption coefficient is then determined by dividing the total absorption by the area of the specimen,

$$\alpha = \frac{A}{S} \qquad (2\text{-}6)$$

where: α = absorption coefficient

A = total absorption, in Sabins, ft^2

S = area of specimen, ft^2

The procedure discussed for acquiring absorption coefficients can be performed with several mounting configurations under ASTA guidelines. This allows for various field applications and material types without opinionated fudge factors. The eight mounting configurations are presented in Figure 2.4. Mountings for most absorptive products, such as glass fiber or foam, are presented in mountings number 1, 2, 4, and 7. Special applications where the absorber is used in a composite wall situation is shown in number 5 and 8. Absorbers used for ventilating duct attenuation should be evaluated by the mounting illustrated in number 6. These specialized mountings aid the acoustical engineer in accurate noise reduction projections. The number 4 mounting is the most common test procedure and allows for a true evaluation of the material itself. The influence on the sound absorption coefficient of mountings with an air space behind the absorptive material is shown in Figure 2.5.

The second test procedure is performed with an impedance tube and is outlined by ASTM Standard C384-58, the "Test for Impedance and Absorption of Acoustical Materials by the Tube Method." The absorption coefficient, for normal (perpendicular) incidence of a sound wave only, is determined by placing a small specimen at one end of a closed tube and generating a pure tone at the other end of the tube. Pure tones at the center frequencies of an octave band are used for this test. When the maxima and minima of the sound pressure is measured inside the tube the absorption coefficients can be computed in accordance with the ASTM procedure. Normal incident absorption coefficients

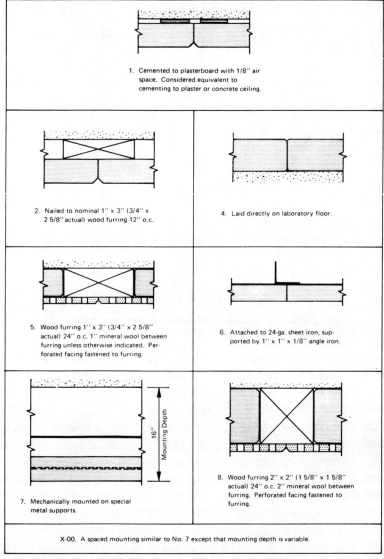

1. Cemented to plasterboard with 1/8" air space. Considered equivalent to cementing to plaster or concrete ceiling.

2. Nailed to nominal 1" x 3" (3/4" x 2 5/8" actual) wood furring 12" o.c.

4. Laid directly on laboratory floor.

5. Wood furring 1" x 3" (3/4" x 2 5/8" actual) 24" o.c. 1" mineral wool between furring unless otherwise indicated. Perforated facing fastened to furring.

6. Attached to 24-ga. sheet iron, supported by 1" x 1" x 1/8" angle iron.

7. Mechanically mounted on special metal supports.

8. Wood furring 2" x 2" (1 5/8" x 1 5/8" actual) 24" o.c. 2" mineral wool between furring. Perforated facing fastened to furring.

X-00. A spaced mounting similar to No. 7 except that mounting depth is variable.

Courtesy of Acoustical and Insulating Materials Association.

Figure 2.4. Laboratory test mountings for sound-absorbing materials.

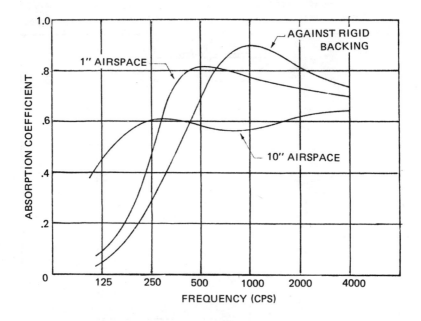

Figure 2.5.

An air space behind a fibrous absorbing material reduces the high-frequency coefficients slightly, but produces a considerable increase in the low-frequency absorption.

and acoustic impedances of materials are conveniently measured by exploring the standing wave pattern in front of a specimen by means of a moving probe microphone. Because the reverberant chamber method is expensive, time consuming, and involves elaborate facilities and large specimen, the impedance tube method is generally used in basic research and development of new acoustical materials. However, absorption coefficients determined by reverberant chamber methods are generally more useful for practical acoustical design than normal incidence absorption coefficients since they represent field conditions with respect to random incidence of sound on the material.

The relationship of the normal (perpendicular) sound absorption coefficient, α_n, and the reverberant (all angles of sound incidence) sound absorption coefficient, α_{rev}, is complex but can be estimated for a given material if relations between these two quantities are established for a material that has similar physical properties, such as porosity, density, and perforation characteristics. Roughly, α_{rev} is about twice the value of α_n at very small values of α_n and approximately equal to it at high values of α_n. Maximum numerical differences of 0.20 to 0.35 between α_n and α_{rev} usually occur at intermediate values of α_n.

THE DENSITY MYTH

It is often reported in the published literature that the low frequency sound absorptive properties of a glass fiber material increase as a function of the density of the material. This notion is incorrect. The sound absorptive characteristics of a material are primarily a function of frequency, and are not related to the material density. Table 2.1 presents the sound absorption coefficients for glass fiber of densities from 1 psf to 6 psf, for a one-inch thickness and a No. 4 mounting. No significant performance changes are observed for the various densities.

Table 2.1
Sound Absorption Coefficient for one-inch thick glass fiber
as a function of density for a No. 4 mounting

Density (psf)	Sound Absorption Coefficient at frequency of						
	125	250	500	1000	2000	4000	N.R.C.
1	.11	.24	.58	.86	.85	.77	.63
1½	.09	.20	.57	.88	.86	.79	.63
2¼	.07	.19	.50	.85	.85	.76	.60
3	.07	.22	.62	.95	.90	.82	.67
4¼	.07	.18	.51	.89	.88	.80	.62
6	.07	.19	.57	.93	.90	.83	.65

THE EFFECT OF THICKNESS

The parameter controlling the frequency performance of sound absorbing materials is the material thickness. Figure 2.6 demonstrates the sound absorption coefficient characteristics of glass fiber for thicknesses ranging from one inch to six inches.

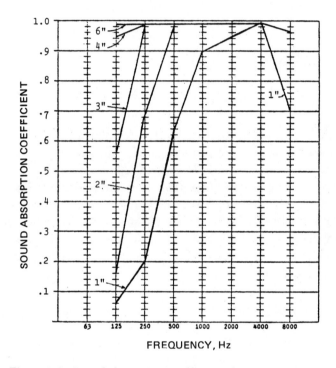

Figure 2.6. Sound absorption coefficients for various thicknesses of glass fiber, 3 psf.

ACOUSTICAL LABORATORIES

Several independent laboratories provide testing services to certify the acoustical performance of materials. A list is provided in Table 2.2.

Table 2.2
Independent acoustical laboratories.

Cedar Knolls Acoustical Laboratory
9 Saddle Road
Cedar Knolls, New Jersey 97927

Geiger & Hamme
Box 1345
Ann Arbor, Michigan 48106

International Acoustical Testing Laboratory
2200 Highcrest Drive
St. Paul, Minnesota 55119

Kodaras Acoustical Laboratory
75-02 51st Avenue
Elmhurst, New York 11373

Riverbank Acoustical Laboratory
1512 Batavia Avenue
Geneva, Illinois 60134

REFERENCES

1. Wiellette, R. E., "Transmission Loss of ¾ Inch Plywood," Cedar Knolls Acoustical Laboratories, August 6, 1971.

2. Thumann, A. and Miller, R. K., *Secrets of Noise Control,* The Fairmont Press, Inc., 2nd ed., 1976.

3. Owens Corning Fiberglas, "Absorption Data on 700 Series," from Geiger & Hamme, Inc. test report, February 24, 1967.

3

Materials for
Special Environments

Generally, the greatest challenges facing the designer of an acoustical enclosure involve solving practical problems related to a basic conceptual design. It may be rather straightforward to compute required acoustical properties for an enclosure. (Complete acoustical design guidelines are presented in subsequent chapters of this book.) But what about enclosure designs for high-temperature environments? Environments with chemical and other contaminants? Protection from physical abuses? These are the real challenges which the designer must meet. Since the feasibility of actual field applications is dependent on the environmental conditions that the acoustical material is exposed to, protecting the acoustical material against physical, thermal, and contaminant abuse is essential to design success. Several methods will be presented in this chapter to solve these practical problems without sacrificing the acoustical integrity of the enclosure system.

MATERIAL FACINGS

Facings may be applied to the exterior surfaces of sound absorptive materials to provide protection against physical and contaminant abuse. The two primary types of protection are:

1. Perforated material facings
2. Film facings

PERFORATED MATERIAL FACINGS

Perforated sheet metal, expanded metal, pegboard, and other materials with an open area facing are commonly used as a protective cover for sound absorptive acoustical materials. The protection provided by these facings is against penetration or abuse by objects, and not saturation prevention of the absorber by airborne contaminants such as oil. Figure 3.1 presents several perforated facing configurations.

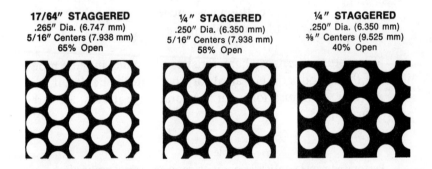

17/64″ STAGGERED
.265″ Dia. (6.747 mm)
5/16″ Centers (7.938 mm)
65% Open

¼″ STAGGERED
.250″ Dia. (6.350 mm)
5/16″ Centers (7.938 mm)
58% Open

¼″ STAGGERED
.250″ Dia. (6.350 mm)
⅜″ Centers (9.525 mm)
40% Open

Courtesy of Harrington & King Perforating Co., Inc.

Figure 3.1. Perforated sheet metal configuration.

If the perforated panel is thin, the principal effect is to reduce the absorption at higher frequencies in inverse proportion to the percentage of open area. The frequency at which this reduction is likely to become apparent can be estimated from the formula:

$$f = \frac{40\,p}{d} \qquad (3\text{-}1)$$

where: f = frequency, Hz
              p = percentage of open area
              d = diameter of the perforations, inches

The openings of the facing and the airspace between the facing and wall interact to form a reactive acoustical system. This system will have a resonant frequency, or Helmholtz frequency at which the system will act as a sound absorber. This frequency is given by:

$$f = \frac{c}{2\pi} \sqrt{\frac{P}{d(L + 1.7R)}}$$ *(3-2)*

where: f = resonant frequency, Hz
              c = speed of sound, ft/sec
                 = 1128 ft/sec at 70° F
              P = perforation ratio: hole area to panel area
              d = distance from panel to wall, inches
              L = panel thickness, inches
              R = radius of hole, inches

The actual resonant characteristics of a panel may be modified by the introduction of an absorptive material behind it.
    Several configurations for perforation patterns are presented in Table 3.1.

Table 3.1
Perforated panel configurations with good acoustical properties[1]

Hole Diameter (in.)	Spacing (In. O.C.)	Notes
3/16	0.5	A
5/32	0.4	
1/8	0.3	B
3/92	0.22	
1/16	0.15	B
1/32	0.08	

Notes:
A   Safe limit for hardboard ("pegboard") material
B   Most suitable for wall materials. Can be painted without clogging holes, and holes are small enough to discourage the jabbing of sharp objects into them.

Sound absorption data for fiberglass with various perforated facings is presented in Table 3.2.

FILM FACINGS

Film facings protect the acoustical material from contaminants such as moisture (oil and water) and air-borne particles (dirt and metal). Limited thermal protection can be gained by using a reflective or aluminized film surface. Common films with their surface weights and tensile modulus as a function of their thickness are presented in Table 3.3. The effect of these films to modify the absorptive performance within the frequency spectrum is controllable. Figure 3.2 depicts how the performance is modified by various thicknesses of a protective film. The thickness of the membrane can improve the performance in a selected frequency giving the specifying engineer the freedom of designing an absorptive configuration for each specific application. Figure 3.3 illustrates the peak performance frequency for each film material in various thicknesses.

Even a very lightweight 0.5 mil film harms high frequency performance and heavier films show progressively more cutoff at frequencies above 1000 Hz. However, at frequencies below 1000 Hz, the presence of a membrane is beneficial and low frequency performance is enhanced.

ADDITIONAL PERFORMANCE REQUIREMENTS

In addition to acoustical design specifications and protection, material selection must often comply with three additional performance requirements:

1. Fire resistance codes
2. Specifications for food processing plants, promulgated by the Food and Drug Administration (FDA), and U.S. Department of Agriculture (USDA)
3. High-temperature environments

Table 3.2
Sound Absorption Coefficients of glass fiber materials with perforated facings

Facing	Thk.	Sound Absorption Coefficient						NRC	Ref
		125	250	500	1000	2000	4000		
1/4" pegboard, 1/4" holes, 1" O.C.	1"	.08	.32	.99	.76	.34	.12	.60	2
Same	2"	.26	.97	.99	.66	.34	.14	.75	2
Same	3"	.49	.99	.99	.69	.37	.15	.75	2
Same	4"	.80	.99	.99	.71	.38	.13	.75	2
Same	5"	.98	.99	.99	.71	.40	.20	.75	2
Same	6"	.95	.99	.98	.69	.36	.18	.75	2
1/8" pegboard, 1/8" holes, 1/8" O.C.	1"	.09	.35	.99	.76	.34	.12	.60	2
24 GA., 3/32" hole, 13% open	2"	.18	.73	.99	.99	.97	.93	.95	3

Table 3.3

Physical properties of common plastic films[4]

Symbol	Material	Thickness In.	Surface Wt. gram/ft²	Tensile Modulus PSI
A	Polyethylene	.0005	1.42	Low
B	Polyester	.0005	1.58	High
C	Aluminized Polyester	.0010	2.88	High
D	Polyester	.0010	2.97	High
E	Polyurethane ("Korel")	.0010	2.98	Very Low
F	Polyvinyl Flouride ("Tedlar")	.0020	5.11	Mod. High
G	Polyester	.0020	6.60	High
H	Polyurethane ("Tuftane")	.0030	7.07	Very Low
I	Polypropylene	.0050	10.75	Medium
J	Polyester	.0050	17.36	High
K	Plasticized Polyvinyl Chloride	.0150	51.29	Mod. Low

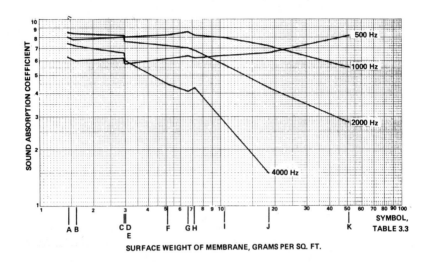

Figure 3.2. Acoustical properties of sound absorptive material as a function of film facing weight.[4]

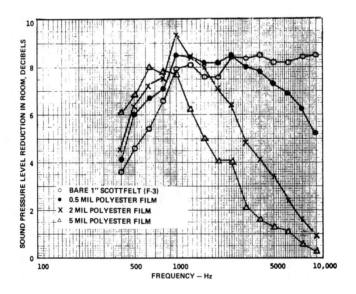

Figure 3.3. Effect of impermeable membranes on sound absorptive properties of acoustical foam.[4]

FIRE CODES[5]

Building construction is under the jurisdiction of the National Fire Protection Association. Local codes may add extra supplemental regulations without altering the basic specification. Local building inspectors play a major role in the acceptance of materials installed. Agents of the Insurance Services inspect and rate buildings with acoustical materials installed to adjust premiums on fire insurance accordingly.

There exists a widely accepted method in fire rating of materials. Underwriters Laboratories, Inc. uses the horizontal tunnel test method, U.L. 723, for evaluating surface burning characteristics of building materials. It is applicable to any type of building material, including all acoustical materials. The test, as defined by U.L. specifications, determines the burning characteristics of the material by evaluating the flame spread over its surface, fuel contributed by its combustion, and the density of smoke developed. The U.L. test method was approved as ANSI A2.5-1970 on April 14, 1970.

The fire hazard classification (F.H.C.) is comprised of the flame spread classification, the fuel contributed, and the smoke developed. The flame spread classification (F.S.C.) is determined as follows:[6]

A.   For materials on which the flame spreads 19½ feet:

1.   In 5½ minutes or less, the classification shall be 100 times 5½ minutes divided by the time in minutes (t) in which the flame spreads 19½ feet (FSC = 550/t).

2.   In more than 5½ minutes but not more than 10 minutes, the classification shall be 100 times 5½ minutes divided by the time in minutes (t) that the flame spreads 19½ feet; plus one-half the difference of 100 minus this result (FSC = 50 + 275/t).

B.   For materials on which the flame spreads less than 19½ feet and then ceases to continue or recedes in a 10-minute test period:

1. When the extreme flame-spread distance (d) is more than 13½ feet and less than 19½ feet, the classification shall be 100 times 5½ minutes times the distance (d) divided by 19½ feet times 10 minutes; plus one-half the difference of 100 minus this result (FSC = 50 + 1.41d).

2. When the extreme flame-spread distance (d) is 13½ feet or less, the classification shall be 100 times the distance (d) divided by 19½ feet (FSC = 5.128d).

The results of the thermocouple and ammeter readings are plotted using identical co-ordinates. Numerical classification is assigned by comparison with the calibration specimens (red oak and asbestos, 100 and 0 respectively).

Manufacturers of acoustical materials and the Insurance Services have adopted a further system using the flame spread classification (F.S.C.) to rate combustible and noncombustible materials. The classification is as follows:

Class	*Flame Spread (F.S.C.)*
1	25 or less
2	26 to 75
3	76 & above

Class 1 materials are considered noncombustible, while classes 2 and 3 are considered combustible. The Insurance Services, who rate buildings by structure, nature of contents and protection, adjust premiums according to the class of building and/or acoustical materials utilized. (Classes A, B and C are sometimes substituted for 1, 2 and 3, respectively.)

Underwriters Laboratories, Factory Mutual Research, and Southwest Research Laboratories test and rate materials on a client basis under ASTM E-84. The U.L. 723 tunnel test, approved as ANSI A2.5-1970, is synonymous with the E-84 test method. Other standards for fire resistance rating of wall, floor, and ceiling materials are presented in U.L. 263 and ASTM E-119. Also, fire ratings for doors and wall systems are commonly presented on a time basis.

Insurance rates are readjusted according to compliance with national fire codes, nature of occupancy, and the fire protection class, rated 2 to 10, best to worst respectively. Rates may be affected up to 100%.

In the case of enclosures with foam lining, the running footage of the building is calculated. The enclosure area is considered as a partitioned wall and its running footage is also calculated. If the footage of the enclosure is less than 25% to 50%, a 10% rate increase in insurance cost can be expected. If the percentage is 50% or more, the increase would be 20%; if it is 100% or over, there is a 40% increase. Where footage equals or exceeds 200%, a 100% rate increase is applied.

General use of foam in a building, especially vertical barriers, would change a noncombustible metal building rating (NC-2) to a combustible frame building rating (wood). A similar condition would occur where combustible spray-on acoustical treatment is utilized. The rating would change from a metal building to a frame building. For example, in a protection class of 3, the base rate of $.125 for a metal building would increase to $1.90, the rate for a frame building. Ceiling-hung combustible baffles or ceiling tile may increase rates 50% to 100%, depending on the amount of concealed area. Trowel-on dampening, a material not yet investigated, would fall under a rate schedule for hazardous conditions. Depending on the severity of the conditions, the rates could increase from 50% to 400%.

A letter requesting a list of approved materials and/or fire ratings was sent to over 200 manufacturers of acoustical materials. Sixty-eight percent of those responding did not present fire ratings of any type in the consumer-available literature. Table 3.4 presents a list of all acoustical manufacturers in the United States known to provide fire ratings for their materials and systems.

FOOD PLANT REQUIREMENTS

FDA regulation has no procedure for prior approval or disapproval of acoustical materials used in food process plants. FDA personnel and individuals throughout industry have, however,

Table 3.4
Manufacturers of fire-rated noise reduction products

MANUFACTURER	Acoustical Panels	Acoustical Wall Systems	Metals	Lead-Loaded Vinyl/Loaded Vinyl	Concrete Block/Ceramics	Foam	Lead	Plastics	Gypsum Board/Particle Board	Silencers/Mufflers	Doors	Spray Absorption	Damping	Acoustical Ceiling Systems	Glass Fiber	Plywood
Aeroacoustic Corporation 1465 Strong Avenue Copiague, NY 11726 (516) 226-4433										•					•	
Air-O-Plastik Corporation Asia Place Carlstadt, NJ 07072 (201) 935-0500						•									•	
Alpro Acoustics Division Structural Systems Corporation P.O. Box 30460 New Orleans, LA 70190 (504) 522-8656	•		•											•		

American Smelting & Refining Co.
150 St. Charles Street
Newark, NJ 07101
(201) 589-0500

Arrow Sintered Products Company
7650 Industrial Drive
Forest Park, IL 60130
(312) 921-7054

Brunswick Corporation
1 Brunswick Plaza
Skokie, IL 60076
(312) 982-6000

Certain-Teed Products Corporation
OSG Group
Valley Forge, PA 19481
(215) 687-5500

Conwed Corporation
2200 Highcrest Road
Saint Paul, MN 55113
(612) 645-6699

Doug Biron Associates, Inc.
P.O. Box 413
Buford, GA 30518
(494) 945-2929

Ferro Corporation
34 Smith Street
Norwalk CT 06852
(203) 853-2123

/more/

Table 3.4 continued

MANUFACTURER	Plywood	Glass Fiber	Acoustical Ceiling Systems	Damping	Spray Absorption	Doors	Silencers/Mufflers	Gypsum Board/Particle Board	Plastics	Lead	Foam	Concrete Block/Ceramics	Lead-Loaded Vinyl/Loaded Vinyl	Metals	Acoustical Wall Systems	Acoustical Panels
Globe Industries, Inc. 2638 E. 126th Street Chicago, IL 60633 (312) 646-1300												●				
Gypsum Association 201 North Wells Street Chicago, IL 60606 (312) 491-1744	●							●								
The Harrington & King Perforating Co. 5655 Fillmore Street Chicago, IL 60644 (312) 626-1800														●		
Holcomb & Hoke Manufacturing Co., Inc. P.O. Box A-33900 Indianapolis, IN 46203 (317) 784-2444					●											

Company															
Koppers Company, Inc. Pittsburgh, PA 15219 (412) 319-3300	•														
Metal Building Interior Products Co. Lakeview Center 1176 E. 38th Street Cleveland, OH 44114 (216) 431-6040		•	•												•
National Cellulose Corporation 12315 Robin Boulevard Houston, TX 77045 (713) 433-6761				•											
Nichols Dynamics, Inc. 740 Main Street Waltham, MA 02154 (617) 891-7707			•									•			
Pittsburgh Corning Corporation Geocoustic Systems 800 Presque Isle Drive Pittsburgh, PA 15239 (412) 261-2900			•												
The Proudfoot Company, Inc. P.O. Box 9 Greenwich, CT 06830 (203) 869-9031										•	•				

/more/

Table 3.4 continued

MANUFACTURER	Plywood	Glass Fiber	Acoustical Ceiling Systems	Damping	Spray Absorption	Doors	Silencers/Mufflers	Gypsum Board/Particle Board	Plastics	Lead	Foam	Concrete Block/Ceramics	Lead-Loaded Vinyl/Loaded Vinyl	Metals	Acoustical Wall Systems	Acoustical Panels
Scott Paper Company Foam Division 1500 E. 2nd Street Chester PA 19013 (215) 876-2551											•					
Singer Partitions, Inc. 444 N. Lake Shore Drive Chicago, IL 60611 (312) 527-3670			•													
Specialty Composites Delaware Industrial Park Newark, DE 19713 (302) 738-6800			•								•		•			

	Stark Ceramics, Inc. P.O. Box 8880 Canton, OH 44711 (216) 488-1211	Starco 1515 Fairview Avenue St. Louis, MO 63132 (314) 429-5650	U.S. Plywood Div. of Champion International 777 Third Avenue New York, NY 10017 (212) 895-8000	Veneered Metals, Inc. P.O. Box 327 Edison, NY 08817 (201) 549-3800
				●
	●			
		●		
		●		
			●	
				●
		●		
			●	

provided much information on materials application in food plants. Based on the best available resources, food process surfaces and areas have been categorized into three classes, with the following generalized requirements for each class:

1. **Intimate Food Contact.** Materials in frequent contact with food materials must be chemically compatible with that particular food. Compatibility may be verified by the Code of Federal Regulations, or by approval of FDA.

2. **Occasional, Nonintimate Food Contact.** No specific chemical requirements are promulgated; however, the materials must be generally nontoxic and cleanable, and not conducive to bacterial growth.

3. **General.** FDA recommended manufacturing practices recommend "smooth and cleanable surfaces." It should also be a requirement of these materials that they be nontoxic.

The most restricting requirement of the implied FDA regulations is regarding the use of sound absorbing materials. Sound absorbers must be porous or fibrous to dissipate acoustical energy. An additional problem encountered specifically in bakeries is accumulation of flour in materials and machinery, leading to potential insect breeding and organic contaminants. Therefore, all joints and seams of acoustical materials must be sealed. Boundary conditions will not influence the noise reduction effectiveness of most materials and designs developed. Any sealant normally used in machine installation in the bakery would be suitable for the noise control installation. Such installation may include inserting a gasket material between the noise control material and the structure, gluing, welding, and calking.

Noise control panels, consisting of stainless steel and glass fiber hermetically sealed in a plastic film not exceeding 2 mils, may generally be used as acoustical walls, with good acoustical performance meeting FDA and USDA requirements for nonintimate food contact usage. Such a surface film can provide protection to the environment from contamination of the material or possible bacterial growth within the material. A 1- to 3-mil facing of Tedlar or aluminized Mylar may be chemically bonded, without the use of adhesives, to a foam structure, and withstand cleaning, to comply with FDA guidelines. A potentially fatal food contaminant, lead, often used in acoustical barrier systems can be replaced with a barium impregnated vinyl sheet which has nearly identical sound attenuation properties.

Sanitary Design Principles. The following guidelines are applicable to the installation of noise control enclosure systems (adapted from "Sanitary Design Principles" by William S. Stinson, *Food Processing,* October 1976.

1. Systems should be designed for thorough washdown with high-temperature (140-180°F) water and detergents as required for proper cleaning. In some plants high pressure (600 psi) water is used.

2. False walls and voids in walls should be avoided, particularly in process areas.

3. Avoid using glass in, above, or near process areas.

4. Construction materials should be selected to resist wear and corrosion and to protect contents from external contamination.

5. Product contact surfaces must be inert, nontoxic, nonporous, smooth (no cracks, crevices, or sharp corners), easily cleaned, nonpeeling, and inert to steam cleaning, hot water, and sanitizing solutions.

6. All inside corners should have internal angles of sufficient radius (¼" or greater) to provide easy cleanability.

7. Painting of product contact and product zone surfaces should be avoided.

8. Exterior of enclosure must be easily cleaned and not retain soil or wash water.

9. Floor attachments should be minimized.

10. Enclosure should be mounted at least 36" from a wall and at least 36" should be allowed between equipment.

11. Continuously weld all support connections.

12. Seal all ends of support members.

13. Floors, walls and ceilings must be smooth, nonpeeling, inert to process and easily cleaned.

14. Floor, wall and ceiling corners should be coved for easy cleaning. Suggest 4" radius.

15. Caulk or seal all wall, floor, and ceiling joints.

16. Structural members must be integral to the supported surface or caulked to it.

17. Avoid painted walls and ceilings, particularly where moisture is involved. Use prefinished, easily cleaned panels, insulated as necessary.

Material Inventory. A survey was conducted inventorying over 200 manufacturers of acoustical materials with products which are applicable to the food industry. The results of this survey are presented in Table 3.5. Where FDA or USDA approval is indicated, it should be recognized that the material(s) involved are approved as food contact surfaces; however, each application of these materials must be reviewed in terms of each specific system or installation.

HIGH TEMPERATURE APPLICATIONS

Acoustical enclosures and barriers are commonly used in conjunction with high temperature noise sources. Typical examples are furnaces, forges, steam piping, and chemical processes. In these cases, the high temperature characteristics of the acoustical materials are most important. In addition to insuring that the material has an adequate fire code rating for the application, the structural integrity and physical properties at the elevated temperature must also be considered. Approximate temperature limits for several common acoustical materials are presented in Table 3.6.

It should also be recognized that the acoustical properties of materials will vary at elevated temperatures. Since the acoustic

Table 3.5
Manufacturers of acoustical products for the food process industry

MANUFACTURER	USDA Approved	FDA Approved	Steam Cleanable	Stainless Steel	Barriers	Faced Absorbers	Mufflers	Pipe Couplings	Enclosures	Damping	Doors
Allied Witan Company 12500 Bellaire Road Cleveland, OH 44135							●				
American Acoustical Products 9 Cochituate Street Natick, MA 01760	●	●			●	●					
Body Guard, Inc. P.O. Box 8338 Columbus, OH 43201		●			●	●			●		
Doug Biron Associates, Inc. P.O. Box 413 Buford, GA 30518				●	●	●	●	●	●	●	
Dow Corning Midland, MI 48640		●								●	
Eckel Industries, Inc. 155 Faucett Street Cambridge, MA 02138		●			●	●					●
Ferro Corporation 34 Smith Street Norwalk, CT 06852	●				●	●			●		
Fluid Kinetics Corporation P.O. Box C.E. Ventura, CA 93001			●				●				
B. F. Goodrich P.O. Box 657 Marietta, OH 45750	●	●			●						●
I.D.E. Processes Corporation 106 Eighty-First Avenue Kew Gardens, NY 11415			●			●	●		●		
Industrial Acoustics Company 1160 Commerce Avenue Bronx, NY 10462									●		
Industrial Noise Control 785 Industrial Drive Elmhurst, IL 60126				●	●	●				●	

/more/

Table 3.5 continued

MANUFACTURER	USDA Approved	FDA Approved	Steam Cleanable	Stainless Steel	Barriers	Faced Absorbers	Mufflers	Pipe Couplings	Enclosures	Damping	Doors
Korfund Dynamics Corporation Cantiaque Road Westbury, NY 11590	•	•		•		•					
Metal Building Interior Company 1176 E. 38th Street Cleveland, OH 44114					•	•					
Mercer Rubber Company 136 Mercer Street Trenton, NJ 08690		•						•			
Martec Associates, Inc. 1645 Oakton Street Des Plaines, IL 60018				•			•				
Noise Control Products, Inc. 969 Lakeville Road New Hyde Park, NY 11040				•	•	•	•				
Noise Measurement and Control Corp. 322 E. Lancaster Avenue Wayne, PA 19087				•	•	•					
Rollform, Inc. P.O. Box 1065 Ann Arbor, MI 48106						•					
Scott Foam Division 1500 E. Second Street Chester, PA 19013		•				•					
Soundcoat, Inc. 175 Pearl Street Brooklyn, NY 11201						•				•	
Specialty Composites Delaware Industrial Park Newark, DE 19711	•			•		•				•	
Titeflex 603 Hendee Street Springfield, MA 01109		•						•			
Vanec 2655 Villa Creek Drive Dallas, TX 75234				•			•				
Veneered Metals, Inc. P.O. Box 327 Edison, NJ 08817		•		•	•					•	

Table 3.6
Approximate temperature limits for acoustical materials[7]

BARRIERS

Steel	800
Aluminum	500
Stainless	2000
Monel and Refractory Brick	2500+
Plastics	300
Wood	250
Damping barrier	350
Mastics	275
Lead	500
Plaster board	500

ABSORBERS

Foam	225
Convoluted foam	225
Fiberglass	500
Mineral Wool	1600
Felt	225
Asbestos	1600
Resonant cavities	2000
Felt metal	2000
Wedges	1600
Ceramic fiber	2000+

FACINGS

Perforated metals	2000
Expanded metals	2000
Metal or synthetic mesh	2000
Perforated hardboard	300

PROTECTIVE FILMS

Poly	300
Mylar	175

wavelength increases with temperature, the thickness of sound absorptive materials must also increase. The thickness of material required will increase in direct proportion to the wavelength increase due to elevated temperatures. The speed of sound as a function of temperature may be computed from:

$$c = 49 \sqrt{R} \qquad (3\text{-}3)$$

where: c = speed of sound, ft/sec
          R = absolute temperature, degrees Rankine
          = 459.7° + °F
          F = temperature, degrees Fahrenheit

The sound wavelength is proportional to sound speed,

$$c = f\lambda$$

where: c = speed of sound, ft/sec
          f = frequency, Hz
          λ = wavelength, ft

EXAMPLE

To effectively absorb sound at a frequency of 125 Hz at room temperatures, a sound absorptive treatment must be 4" thick. What thickness of sound absorptive material would be required for this case with the temperature elevated to 3000° F?

ANSWER

At room temperature (70°F), the speed of sound is 1128 ft/sec. Assuming a maximum temperature of 3000°F occurs, the sound speed will increase to 2880 ft/sec, or 250%. It follows that the minimum effective thickness for a sound absorptive treatment would be 10".

REFERENCES

1. Egan, M.D., *Concepts in Architectural Acoustics,* McGraw-Hill, 1972.
2. Warring, R. H. (Ed.), *Handbook of Noise and Vibration Control,* Trade and Technical Press, Ltd., 1973.
3. "Fiberglas Acoustical Insulating Materials for Wall Treatments," Owens-Corning Fiberglas Corp., Toledo, Ohio, 1971.

4. Powers, W. R., and Rudinoff, C. D., "The Noise Box Test," presented at NOISEXPO, April 21, 1975.
5. Montone, W. V., "Fire Resistance Codes and Ratings," Proceedings of the Technical Program, NOISEXPO 1976, pp 231-233.
6. Private communications with Underwriters Laboratories, Inc.
7. "Noise Control Enclosures" product literature published by Webster Products Company, Santa Ana, California.
8. "Noise Control Solutions for the Food Industry," Southeast Acoustics Institute, 1977.
9. Miller, R. K., "Acoustical Materials for the Food Process Industry," *Proceedings* Noise Con 73, October 1973, pp 519-522.

4

The Acoustical Wall

The most fundamental approach to noise reduction is to interpose a wall between the sound source and receiver. The wall may take the form of:

1. an enclosure of the noise source (machine),

2. the enclosure of the receiver (employee), or

3. a barrier between the two.

The noise reduction, or difference between the sound levels on either side of the wall, will vary depending upon which of these constructions is employed; however, the physical acoustical properties of the wall are the key element in the calculation of the noise reduction for all three of these designs. The basic acoustical properties of a wall are discussed in this chapter. Applications of these principles for enclosures and barriers are discussed in Chapters 5, 6, and 9.

When a sound wave strikes a wall, the wall is set into motion. This vibration, in turn, causes the air on the other side of the partition to be set into motion and sound is radiated as though this partition were now a sound source. This new sound field will have less energy since much of the energy of the incident wave was spent in forcing the partition to vibrate.

MASS LAW

Newton's second law of motion informs us that the force required to set a wall in motion is equal to the product of its mass times its acceleration. The force exerted by the pressure associated with a sound wave increases in proportion to its frequency. With these two facts, one can intuitively understand that the theoretical transmission loss of a wall will be proportional to its mass and dependent upon the frequency of the sound wave. Analyzing a wall as an "ideal limp mass," the transmission loss is given by:

$$TL = 20 \log W + 20 \log f - 33 \qquad (4\text{-}1)$$

where: TL= transmission loss, dB
            W= surface weight, pounds per square foot
            f= frequency, Hertz

This equation, known as the "mass law," indicates that the transmission loss increases 6 dB each time the weight is doubled and 6 dB each time the frequency is doubled.

REAL WALLS

The transmission loss of limp wall systems, such as lead barriers, follow the mass law reasonably well. Most common building walls, however, are not truly limp, and do not behave in the theoretical manner. Factors influencing the transmission loss are:

1. stiffness
2. resonances
3. damping
4. coincidence effects

These four parameters, along with the mass, influence the sound transmission loss characteristics of a wall in different frequency regions. For analysis purposes, the transmission loss characteristics of a wall may be separated into three regions, as shown in Figure 4.1.

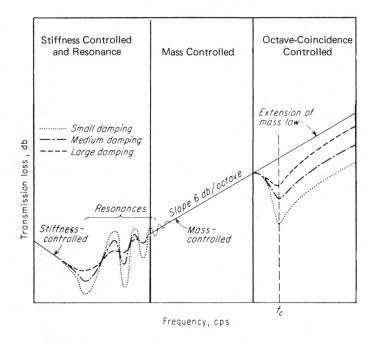

**Figure 4.1. Generalized performance of an acoustical wall,
showing three regions of transmission loss performance.
The critical frequency is f_c.**[1]

The critical coincidence frequency, f_c, is the frequency
where the wavelength of sound in a panel is the same as that in
air. This frequency may be computed from:

$$f_c = \frac{k}{w} \qquad (4\text{-}2)$$

where: f_c = critical frequency, Hertz

k = material constant (from Table 4.1)
Hz — lb/ft^2

w = surface weight, ft^2

The critical coincidence frequency may also be determined
from Figure 4.2.

Table 4.1
Density, internal damping factors, and products of surface density and critical frequency for common building materials[2]

Material	$\rho m,$ lb/ft^3	Constant Hz-lb/ft^2	Internal damping factor at 1,000 Hz η
Aluminum	170	7,000	10^{-4}–10^{-2}
Brick	120–140	7,000–12,000	0.01
Concrete, dense poured	150	9,000	0.005–0.02
Concrete (clinker) slab plastered on both sides, 2 in. thick	100	10,000	0.005–0.02
Masonry block:			
Hollow cinder (nominal 6 in. thick)	50	4,750	0.005–0.02
Hollow cinder, 5/8 in. sand plaster each side (nominal 6 in. thick)	60	5,220	0.005–0.02
Hollow dense concrete (nominal 6 in. thick)	70	4,720	0.007–0.02
Hollow dense concrete, sand-filled voids (nominal 6 in. thick)	108	8,650	Varies with frequency
Solid dense concrete (nominal 4 in. thick)	110	11,100	0.012
Fir timber	40	1,000	0.04
Glass	156	7,800	0.001–0.01
Lead:			
Chemical or tellurium	700	124,000 (approx.)	0.015
Antimonial (hard)	700	104,000	0.002
Plaster, solid, on metal or gypsum lath	108	5,000	0.005–0.01
Plexiglas or Lucite	70	7,250	0.002
Steel	480	20,000	10^{-4}–10^{-2}
Gypsum board (½ to 2 in.) . . .	43	4,500	0.01–0.03
Plywood (¼ to 1¼ in.)	40	2,600	0.01–0.04
Wood waste materials bonded with plastic, 5 lb/ft[2]	48	15,000	0.005–0.01

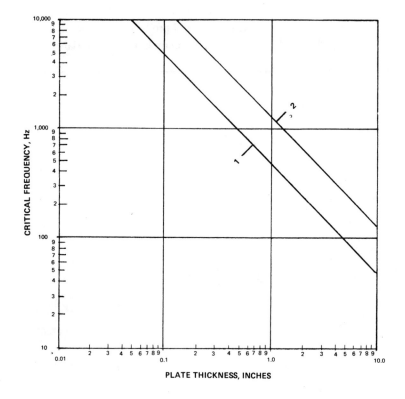

**Figure 4.2 Critical frequency vs. plate thickness for
thin homogenous, isotropic plates[3]
1 – Aluminum or steel
2 – Gypsum board**

ESTIMATION OF TRANSMISSION LOSS

The transmission loss of a material may be estimated using the generalized model of Figure 4.3, as follows:

   1.   The TL for frequencies below the plateau is computed from:

$$TL = 20 \log(W) + K \qquad\qquad (4\text{-}3)$$

where W= Surface weight of material in pounds per square foot

K= Frequency dependent constant from Table 4.2

$$(= 20 \log(f) - 33)$$

Table 4.2
Constant for equation

	Octave band center frequency, Hz							
	63	125	250	500	1000	2000	4000	8000
K, dB	3	9	15	21	27	33	39	46

2. When the calculated TL value, using Equation 4-3, reaches the value of the plateau height, the TL will equal the plateau height value for the next three octave bands. The plateau height for various materials may be found in Table 4.3.

Table 4.3
Surface density and plateau height values
for various materials

Type	Surface density $(lbs/ft^2$ per inch)	Plateau height (dB)
Aluminum	14	29
Brick	11	37
Concrete	12	38
Fir Plywood	3	19
Glass	13	27
Lead	59	56
Sand Plaster	9	30
Steel	40	40
Masonry Block	6	30

3.   Above the plateau, the TL will increase by the rate of 6 dB per octave. (See Figure 4.3.)

Note: This method of estimation is based on the method of Watters, and presented by Beranek.[1] In the original method, a different plateau breadth was used for various materials, and the TL was assumed to increase at 10 dB/octave above the plateau. The simplified method presented here will produce more conservative (lower) TL values.

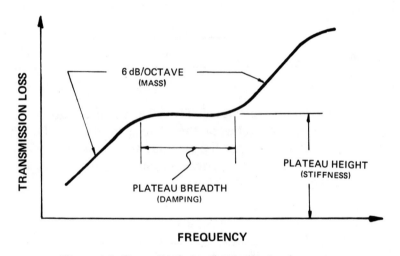

Figure 4.3. Generalized sound transmission loss curve used for TL estimation

DOUBLE WALLS

A double wall is an acoustical barrier constructed of two panels separated by an air space.

The sound transmission loss, TL, of a double wall for mid-frequencies is approximately equal to the TL of a single wall equal in weight to the two walls plus an air space correction factor as shown in Figure 4.4. If the space between the walls is 12 inches or more, the overall TL is approximately the sum of the TL for each wall.

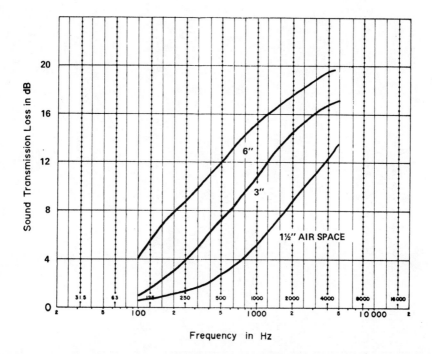

Figure 4.4. Increase in transmission loss of double wall
due to air space

The transmission loss will be reduced at two frequencies:

1. The **double wall resonance**, where the panels respond
   as two masses coupled by a spring (air). This frequency is given by:

$$f = \frac{170}{d}\ \frac{w_1 + w_2}{w_1 w_2} \qquad (4\text{-}4)$$

where $w_{1,2}$ = surface weight of wall, pounds per
                    square foot

       d = cavity dimension, inches

The double wall resonance can also be determined
from the nomograph of Figure 4.5.

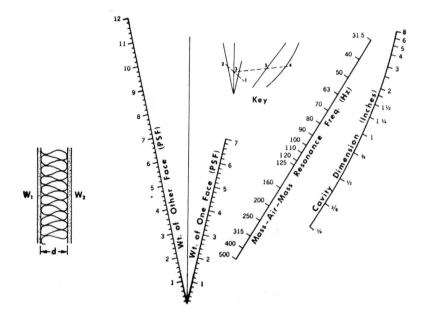

Figure 4.5. Mass-air-mass resonance nomograph[4]

2.   The **critical coincidence frequency**, as previously discussed.

The response parameters of a double wall are summarized in Figure 4.6.

AIR SPACE SOUND ABSORPTION

For a double wall construction, the Sound Transmission Class (STC) of a wall will increase with the weight of the sound absorptive material in the air space. Table 4.4 shows the increasing sound transmission loss for a 5/8-inch sheetrock and metal stud wall with various layers of sound absorptive material in the air space.

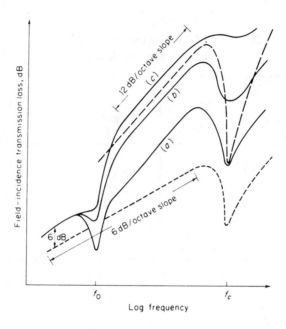

Figure 4.6
Schematic transmission loss for a double wall with identical panels, and no
flanking transmission, indicating the controlling factors. The lower (dashed
curve) is the field-incidence transmission loss of a single panel, while the
upper dashed curve is twice this (in decibels). The double-wall resonance
frequency is f_o and the critical frequency of the panel is f_c. Curve *a* is for
no added absorptive material in the cavity, and curve *b* is for some. Curve
c is for a cavity uniformly filled with absorptive material.[3]

COMPOSITE WALLS

Generally, walls are not constructed of a single material, but will
have openings, windows, doors, etc. To calculate the noise reduction of a composite wall, it is necessary to use the average
sound transmission loss value of the wall. The average transmission coefficient is first computed:

Table 4.4

**The effect of sound absorptive material in
the air space of a double wall[5]**

Thickness inches	Density (PCF)	Weight (PSF)	Standard Transmission Class (STC)
0	0	0	39
1	4	0.33	43
1½	3	0.38	45
2	4	0.67	46
3	3	0.75	46
3	4	1.0	48
4	4	1.33	48

$$\bar{\tau} = \frac{\sum\limits_i \tau_1 S_1}{\sum\limits_i S_i} = \frac{\tau_1 S_1 + \tau_2 S_2 + \tau_3 S_3 + \ldots + \tau_n S_n}{A} \qquad (4\text{-}5)$$

where: τ = average transmission coefficient (see Equation 4-2)

   τ_i = transmission coefficient of each wall element

   S_i = area of each wall element, ft^2

   A = total area of wall, ft^2

The average sound transmission loss is then calculated from:

$$TL_{avg} = 10 \log \frac{1}{\bar{\tau}} \qquad (4\text{-}6)$$

where: TL_{avg} = average sound transmission loss of wall, dB

   $\bar{\tau}$ = average transmission coefficient

The average sound transmission loss may also be calculated by reference to the graph of Figure 4.7, which is based on the difference in transmission losses between two wall materials, and the total area occupied by the "weaker" element. An opening or hole in a wall should be analyzed as having a sound transmission loss of zero.

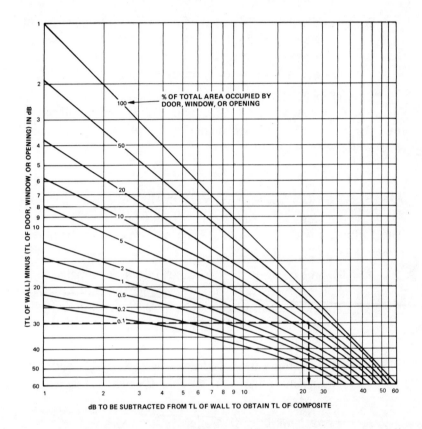

Figure 4.7. Transmission loss of composite walls

SOUND LEAKS

To provide maximum acoustical effectiveness, it is necessary that an acoustical wall or barrier be absolutely air tight. Even a slight opening, as small as 1/32 inch, around a door or window will cause noticeable degradation of a noise reduction structure. Two methods are commonly employed to identify sound leakage paths:

1. A "light test" may be used, where a person inside a dark enclosure will observe for traces of light which will seep through openings.

2. The "dollar bill" test is often utilized to check the effectiveness of door and window seals. If a dollar bill is inserted in a closed door, one should not be able to remove it if the door is properly gasketed.

Several examples of seals for doors and walls are shown in Figure 4.8. Porous materials and open-cell foams should not be used for acoustical seals, since they offer very low sound transmission loss characteristics.

ADHESIVES FOR SOUND CONTROL MATERIALS

The following list presents adhesives and sealants applicable to noise control constructions:[7]

1. **Rigid composite (skin/core) panel construction:** Solvent- and water-based neoprene contact adhesives; epoxy and urethane curable liquids; solvent-based modified phenolic thermosetting adhesives; thermosetting film adhesives.

2. **Vinyl laminations:** Nitrile adhesives; vinyl copolymer laminating adhesives; curable epoxies, urethanes and polyesters.

3. **Lead laminations:** Generally compatible with all of the previously mentioned adhesive suggestions.

4. **Urethane foam, fiber glass:** All of the previously mentioned adhesives and, in addition, solvent- and water-based and pressure sensitive film adhesives; elastomeric, one-side-applied insulation adhesives; hot melt assembly adhesives.

5. **Installation:** Preapplied pressure sensitive film adhesives; neoprene contact adhesives; nitrile adhesives.

6. **Sealing:** Room-temperature-gunnable butyls (also acrylics); two-part curable polysulfides (also poly-

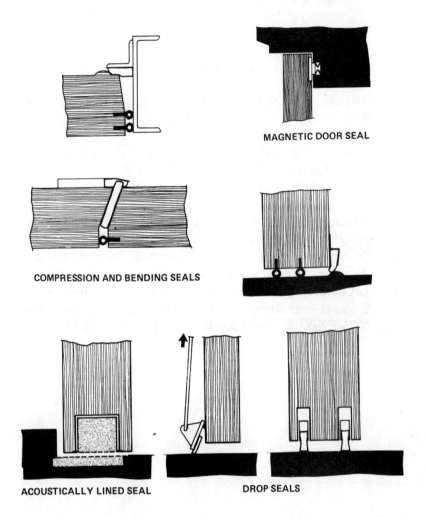

**Figure 4.8. Examples of acoustical seals
for doors and walls**[6]

urethanes); hot-extruded elastomerics and hot melts; profiled extruded butyl tape.

REFERENCES

1. Beranek, L. L. (ed), *Noise Reduction,* McGraw-Hill, 1960.
2. Beranek, L. L., *Noise and Vibration Control,* McGraw-Hill, 1971.
3. Dameron, "Sound Control for Aluminum Curtain Walls," AMA, January, 1973.
4. Fader, B., "Mass-Air-Mass Resonance Nomograph," *Sound and Vibration,* August, 1970, p. 25.
5. Ellwood, E. E., "Noise Control Effects of Rock Wool," *Pollution Engineering,* v. 5, n. 8, August 1973, p. 27.
6. Sound Research Laboratories Limited, *Practical Building Acoustics,* Spon, Ltd., London, 1976.
7. LeCompte, R. A., and Grover, M. M., "Adhesives and Sealants for Sound Control Materials," *Proceedings of NOISEXPO 75,* April 30–May 2, 1975, pp. 130-31.

5

Applications of Employee Enclosures

Not to be overlooked as a method of reducing an employee's noise exposure is an enclosure which isolates the operator from the noise environment. The advantage of this approach is that it is often many times more cost effective to build a relatively small enclosure for employees than to enclose or redesign large or numerous items of equipment. The enclosure also serves to protect the employee from other unfavorable aspects of the work environment, and may result in increased productivity in some cases. Numerous factors, including machine maintainability, safety, heat stress, and productivity enter into the determination of the feasibility of employee enclosures. This chapter illustrates the application of these factors along with other design factors for employee enclosures.

When an employee (receiver) is isolated from a noise source by a wall or enclosure, the amount of noise attenuation depends upon four factors:

1. The sound transmission loss of the wall between the noise source and receiver.

2. The surface area of the wall.

3. The acoustical characteristics of the source room.

4. The acoustical characteristics of the receiving room.

The sound transmission loss characteristics of a wall are discussed in Chapter 2 of this book. In Chapter 12, transmission loss data is presented for a variety of wall constructions. These values may be used in the calculations presented in this chapter.

It is probably obvious that a wall with a relatively small area will transmit less total sound energy than will a wall with a relatively large area, even though each square foot of the wall has the same TL value.

When a noise source is enclosed with a material with hard (acoustically reflective) interior surfaces, sound levels will build up within the enclosure due to sound being reflected from wall to wall within the enclosure. This reverberant effect will cause interior sound levels to be higher than they would be without the enclosure, and overall noise reduction is decreased.

Similarly, the sound level in the receiving room will be influenced by the amount of acoustic absorption in the room, that is, the sound pressure level will be relatively high in a "live" receiving room having little or no acoustic absorption whereas it will be relatively low in a "dead" receiving room having large amounts of acoustic absorption.

The following section presents an analysis of the acoustical properties of a room, which may be used to assess sound propagation behavior within either a "source room" or "receiver room." Next, a series of equations are presented to allow calculation of the noise reduction due to an acoustical enclosure system.

The value of the room constant, R, will establish the attenuation characteristics of sound as one moves away from a noise source. Figure 5.1 shows the attenuation of sound as a function of distance for various values of R. From the figure, it is seen that the sound level will decrease as one moves from one to five feet away from a sound source in a very reverberant room (R < 500). Beyond a distance of one to five feet, however, the sound level will attenuate only slightly as one moves further from the source. For higher values of the room constant, sound will attenuate more noticeably at greater distances from a noise source. Outdoors (R= ∞), sound levels will attenuate at a rate of 6 decibels for each doubling of distance from a noise source.

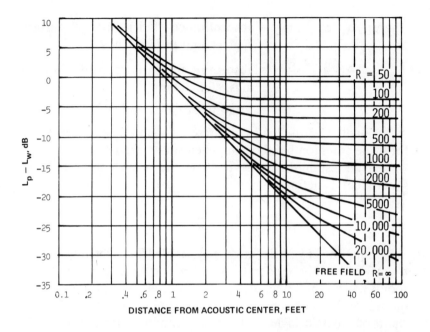

**Figure 5.1. Effect of distance and room constant
on sound pressure levels within a room**

ROOM ACOUSTICS

To assess room acoustical properties, the average sound absorption coefficient of the room is first needed. The sound absorption coefficient, $\overline{\alpha}$, represents the ratio of the sound absorbed by a material surface to the sound incident on the surface, ranging from zero to one, as discussed in Chapter 2. The average sound absorption, $\overline{\alpha}$, of a room is the spatial average of the coefficients of each room surface:

$$\overline{\alpha} = \frac{S_1\alpha_1 + S_2\alpha_2 \ldots S_n\alpha_n + A_1 + A_2 \ldots A_n}{S} \qquad (5\text{-}1)$$

where: $\alpha_1, \alpha_2 \ldots \alpha_n$ = absorption coefficient for each surface type at a given frequency

$S_1, S_2 \ldots S_n$ = absorption units of occupants, furnishings, etc., Sabins.

S = total surface area, in feet^2

Chapter 12 of this book presents sound absorption values for some common building and enclosure materials.

After establishing the $\bar{\alpha}$ value the room constant, R, in square feet, is defined as:

$$R = \frac{S\alpha}{1-\alpha} \qquad (5\text{-}2)$$

Equation (5-2) is most applicable for relatively square rooms with only moderate sound absorption ($\bar{\alpha} < .15$). For rooms having the sound absorbent material concentrated on one or two walls, while one pair or two pairs of parallel surfaces in the room remain highly reflective, a modified form of the Fitzroy equation[1] may be applied to compute the room constant:

$$R = \frac{S}{\frac{1}{S}\left[\frac{x}{\alpha_x} + \frac{y}{\alpha_y} + \frac{z}{\alpha_z}\right] - 1} \qquad (5\text{-}3)$$

where: x,y,z = wall surface areas, ft^2

$\alpha_x, \alpha_y, \alpha_z$ = sound absorption coefficients of each set of parallel walls

S = total surface area, ft^2

R = room constant, ft^2

The American National Standard Institute S1.1−1960 (R-1971) defines the reverberation time of a room as the time required for the mean-square sound-pressure level therein, originally in a steady state, to decrease 60 dB after the source is stopped. By measuring the reverberation time, R can be calculated as follows:

$$R = \frac{S}{(TS/.049V) - 1} \qquad (5\text{-}4)$$

where: S = total room surface area, square feet

V = volume of room, feet^3

T = reverberation time, seconds

ENCLOSURE NOISE REDUCTION CALCULATION

The sound pressure level in a room with a receiver, separated by a partition from a room with a sound source, as shown in Figure 5.2, may be calculated from any of the following three equations:

$$L_p(r) = L_w(s) - TL + 10 \log \left(\frac{S}{R_s} \right) + 10 \log \left(\frac{1}{S} + \frac{4}{R_r} \right) + 10 \quad (5\text{-}5)$$

$$L_p(r) = L_p(s) - TL + 10 \log \left(\frac{S}{4} \right) + 10 \log \left(\frac{1}{S} + \frac{4}{R_r} \right) \quad (5\text{-}6)$$

$$L_p(r) = L_p(s) - TL + 10 \log \left(\frac{1}{4} + \frac{S}{R_r} \right) \quad (5\text{-}7)$$

where: $L_p(r)$ = sound pressure level in receiver room, measured near the wall surface, dB re .0002 microbar

$L_w(s)$ = sound power level in source room, dB re 10^{-12} watt

$L_p(s)$ = sound pressure level in source room, dB re .0002 microbar

TL = sound transmission loss of wall, dB

S = surface area of wall, ft^2

R_s = room constant of source room, ft^2

R_r = room constant of receiver room, ft^2

From Equation (5-7), it is noted that the noise reduction is equal to the sound transmission loss when the ratio of the wall surface area to the room constant of the receiving room is equal to 3/4, or

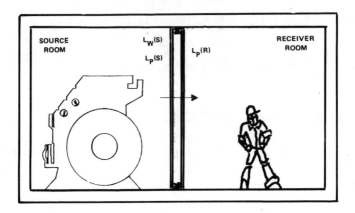

**Figure 5.2. Noise source and receiver,
separated by a partition**

$$NR = L_p(s) - L_p(r) = TL \qquad (5-8)$$

when

$$\frac{S}{R_r} = \frac{3}{4} \qquad (5-9)$$

When the values of S and R_r are nearly equal, Equation (5-8) provides a reasonable estimation of a wall's noise reduction. Equation (5-8) will result in an underdesigned wall (NR < TL), however, if the receiver room is relatively reverberant. For example, when $R_r = 0.1S$,

$$NR = L_p(s) - L_p(r) = TL - 10 \qquad (5-10)$$

For the case where sound is transmitted to the outside ($R \rightarrow \infty$), Equation (5-7) reduces to

$$NR = L_p(s) - L_p(r) = TL + 6 \qquad (5-11)$$

APPROXIMATE CALCULATION METHOD

The approximate noise reduction provided by a wall isolating a receiver from a noise source may also be calculated from:[2]

$$NR = TL + C \qquad (5\text{-}12)$$

where: $NR = L_p(s) - L_p(r)$

$L_p(s)$ = sound pressure level in sound source room, dB re .0002 microbar

$L_p(r)$ = sound pressure level in receiver room, dB re .0002 microbar

TL = sound transmission loss of wall, dB

C = correction factor, as defined in Table 5.1.

Table 5.1
Approximate correction term for use in
the relationship $NR = TL + C$[2]

Total Surface Area Inside Receiving Room Divided by Area of Common Wall or Floor	*Acoustic Treatment of Receiving Room*			
	Condition 1	*Condition 2*	*Condition 3*	*Condition 4*
1.4–2.7	10 dB	– 7 dB	– 4 dB	– 2 dB
2.8–5.5	– 7	– 4	– 2	+ 1
5.6–10	– 4	– 2	+ 1	+ 3
11–21	– 2	+ 1	+ 3	+ 4
22–43	+ 1	+ 3	+ 4	+ 5
44–80	+ 3	+ 4	+ 5	+ 6

Condition 1:   No significant amount of sound absorption material (less than that of Condition 2).

Condition 2:   10–25% of total room area covered with ¾ in.–1 in. thick sound absorption material.

Condition 3:   26–50% of total room area covered with ¾ in.–1 in. thick sound absorption material; or 10–30% of total room area covered with 1½ in.–2 in. thick sound absorption material.

Condition 4:   Over 50% of total room area covered with ¾ in.–1 in. thick sound absorption material; or over 30% of total room area covered with 1½ in.–2 in. thick sound absorption material.

ACOUSTICAL EFFECTIVENESS

While it is relatively easy to reduce industrial noise levels to below 90 dBA using an employee enclosure, the true measure of acoustical effectiveness is the total reduction in employee noise exposure which is achieved by an enclosure. If an employee spends very little time in a quiet enclosure, obviously it is not effective.

A noise dose, D, is defined as the actual exposure time divided by the allowable exposure time. The allowable exposure time, from Table G-16 of the OSHA regulation is given in Table 5.2. The employee noise exposure exceeds the OSHA limits if the noise dose exceeds unity (1), or 100%.

$$D = \frac{C}{T} \qquad (5\text{-}14)$$

where   D = noise dose
$\quad\quad$ C = actual duration of exposure in hours
$\quad\quad$ T = noise exposure limit in hours

Where the daily exposure is due to two or more noise levels, the ratio for each level is added to compute the total noise dose:

$$D = \frac{C_1}{T_1} + \frac{C_2}{T_2} + \ldots \ldots \frac{C_n}{T_n} \qquad (5\text{-}15)$$

In most industrial operations, employees are exposed to varying sound levels, due to either varying modes of operation of a single machine or due to movement throughout a work area and exposure to several items of equipment. Where sound level exposure varies, it is necessary to evaluate the exposure time to each individual sound level environment as a function of an employee's typical daily task routine in order to correctly assess the daily noise dose.[3, 4, 5, 6]

To assess the effectiveness of an enclosure, it is necessary to compute both an employee's normal daily noise dosage and also his noise dosage for the work routine which includes utilization of the acoustical enclosure. If the acoustical enclosure does not reduce an employee's daily noise dose to below unity, and hearing protection must be worn, should the enclosure be

Table 5.2
Permissible noise exposure times

Sound Level (dBA)	Time (hrs)	Sound Level (dBA)	Time (hrs)
90	8.00	103	1.32
91	6.97	104	1.15
92	6.07	105	1.00
93	5.28	106	0.87
94	4.60	107	0.77
95	4.00	108	0.67
96	3.48	109	0.57
97	3.03	110	0.50
98	2.83	111	0.43
99	2.25	112	0.38
100	2.00	113	0.33
101	1.73	114	0.28
102	1.52	115	0.25

installed anyway? Recent rulings of the Occupational Safety and Health Review Commission (OSAHRC) have indicated that noise control measures should be undertaken, if technically and economically feasible, if significant noise reduction can be achieved, even if sound levels are not reduced to below the 90 dBA limit. A level of noise reduction which is considered "significant" may be taken as 2 dBA, since that value is the allowable tolerance (for middle range frequencies) for the Type 2 sound level meter, which is called for in the OSHA noise regulation. Translating from a 2 dBA level of significance, an equivalent reduction in exposure time would be two hours.

ENCLOSURE TYPES

Employee enclosures may be of various designs, including four-sided, three-sided, or multiple opening enclosures. In most cases, these enclosures do not need to be elaborate control rooms, since only a 5–15 dBA noise reduction is required, and this may easily be achieved with a simple enclosure of relatively light construction.

If a four-sided enclosure is applicable, windows, ventilation, and communication equipment should be installed. This type of booth can be used where the operator does not rely on audible detection techniques for operation. It should not be used under conditions in which its presence may endanger workers with possible entrapment or booth collapse as a result of inherent production hazards. This kind of enclosure is ideal for control rooms and for rest area locations where there are often employees present who are not directly involved in the area operations and are present for environmental benefits.

A three-sided, or lean-to type enclosure is applicable where only a small noise reduction is required. Such an enclosure provides safety as well as production advantages. Greater accessibility to exit reduces the potential for entrapment. In operations which require that the operator be able to hear the machine, this type of enclosure may reduce sound levels to an acceptable level while permitting effective audible monitoring of the operation.

A multi-sided, multiple opening booth or enclosure can be used to achieve to adequate noise attenuation while also allowing the operator to hear his machine as necessary, but at a lower intensity. The enclosure may have several openings or exits for accessibility, and can be equipped with window viewing ports as required.

Design sketches showing several employee enclosures are presented in Figures 5.3 through 5.7.

EMPLOYEE ENCLOSURE DESIGN

When designing an employee enclosure, the following important factors must be considered:

1. Location
2. Size
3. Visibility
4. Accessibility
5. Proximity

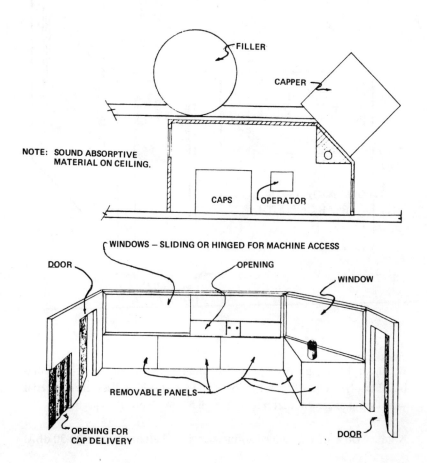

**Figure 5.3. Acoustical enclosure for seamer operator
in beverage plant**

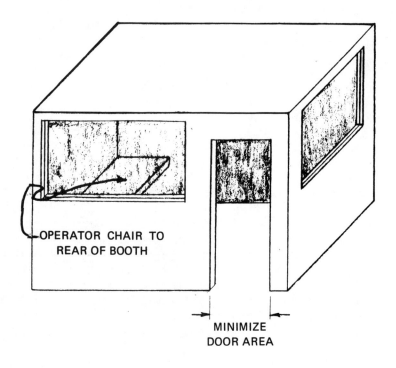

Booth of 1.5 pound per square foot minimum sheet metal or non-combustible plywood. All non-window surfaces of 4-inch glass fiber material with facing of screen, perforated sheet metal (40% open) or pegboard.

Note: Door may be added to increase sound attenuation to 20-30 dBA.

**Figure 5.4. Employee acoustical booth providing an estimated
10 dBA sound attenuation**

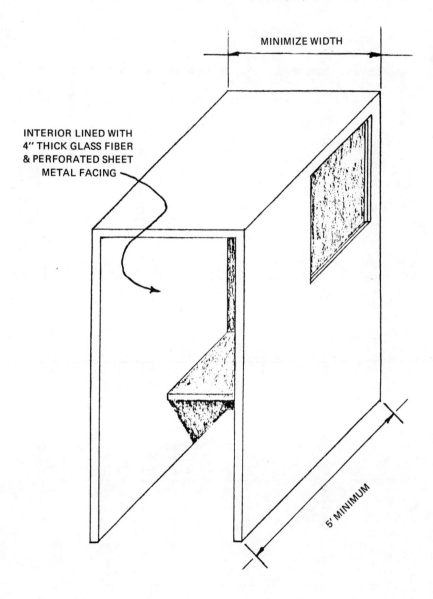

Figure 5.5. Three-sided operator enclosure

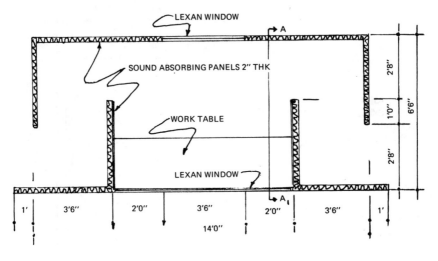

PLAN VIEW

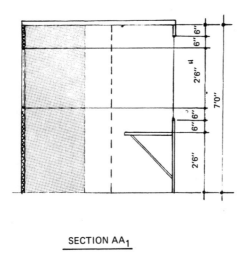

SECTION AA₁

Figure 5.6. Employee enclosure and work station

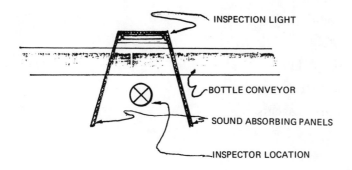

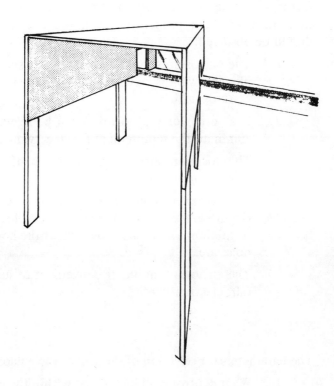

Figure 5.7. Three-sided booth for bottle inspectors

    6.   Comfort

    7.   Productivity

    8.   Safety

    9.   Air quality

   10.   Heat stress

   11.   Physical agents

LOCATION

The location of an enclosure is an initial and important design factor, affecting both the effectiveness and cost of the installation. In selecting a proper location, the following guidelines should be observed:

1. The enclosure should be located in a space where employees will have visual and physical access to the work operations.

2. If a corner or wall location can be selected, this may eliminate the requirement for one, two, or three walls.

3. The location should not restrict paths of material flow or employee mobility.

4. The location should be convenient to the operations requiring the most attention by employees in order to minimize time spent outside of the booth in a high noise area.

5. The enclosure should be convenient to supply systems (air, electricity, etc.).

SIZE

The parameters for selection of the size of the enclosure include:

1. What controls will be located within the enclosure

2. What operations will be performed in the enclosure

3. How many men will inhabit the enclosure (average and maximum number)

4. What spatial access may be necessary for maintenance within the enclosure

5. What physical constraints are dictated by the enclosure location

The size of the enclosure will, more than any other factor, dictate the total cost of the enclosure. Typical costs of enclosure construction are provided in Chapter 10.

VISIBILITY

The installation of windows is not incompatible with the acoustical requirements of an enclosure, providing that proper design guidelines are recognized. While window materials provide virtually no sound absorption, areas of up to 60% of the entire enclosure surface area may be window areas without causing an excessively reverberant interior environment, if all other interior surfaces are of a highly absorptive material.

The relatively light weight of windows, when compared to other enclosure wall constructions will allow windows to be the "weak link" in isolating external sound. Adequate sound isolation, however, may be achieved, if window materials and construction are selected which are consistent with the noise reduction requirements of the enclosure. Figure 5.8 shows typical noise reduction values of some common window constructions. To insure acoustical effectiveness, it is extremely important that windows be properly gasketed.

Window materials must also be carefully selected with regard to functional requirements. Table 5.3 compares the relative qualities of five window glazing materials commonly used for enclosures.

ACCESSIBILITY

Generally, an employee enclosure may be exited within one or two seconds when operational attention is required, and accessibility problems would not be expected to be significant with a conventional employee enclosure. Careful placement of doors can serve to minimize potential accessibility problems.

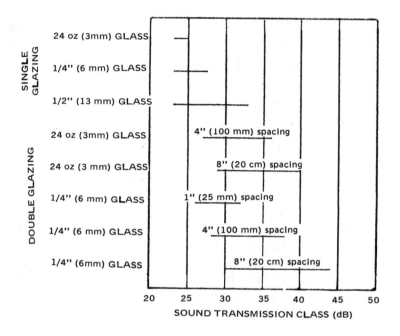

**Figure 5.8. Ranges of sound insulation of single
and double glazed windows[7]**

PROXIMITY

The placement of employees within an enclosure may serve to isolate them physically, audibly, and visually from the machinery or operations which they control. The extent of this isolation may be the dominant factor in establishing the feasibility of this approach to noise control. Where operations require intimate interaction between a single machine and its operator, or where an employee's job requires attendance of a large number of machines within a large area, an employee enclosure may not be an appropriate design solution for noise control. With these design problems, the use of closed circuit television cameras, machine control monitors, and intercom systems may be considered.

Table 5.3
Comparison chart showing relative qualities of
five window glazing materials
commonly used in enclosures

	Acrylics	*Homalite-G*	*Poly-Carbonate*	*Laminated Wire Glass*	*Tempered Glass*
Hot Metal	Poor	Excellent	Poor	Poor	Poor
Sparks	Poor	Excellent	Poor	Poor	Poor
Acid Chemicals	Poor	Excellent	Poor	Excellent	Excellent
Solvent Chemicals	Fair	Excellent	Fair	Excellent	Excellent
Pitting Denting	Poor	Excellent	Poor	Poor	Poor
Optical Quality	Good	Excellent	Good	Good	Excellent
Weight	Light	Light	Light	Heavy	Heavy
Impact Resistance	Fair	Fair	Excellent	Good	Excellent
Heat Resistance	Good	Good	Fair	Good	Good

COMFORT

Industry is showing an increasing attention to employee comfort, as evidenced by the growing number of plants which are air conditioned. Part of the reason is that employees are becoming more particular about their environment. As people are beginning to consider air-conditioning in their homes as a necessity rather than a luxury, they are also demanding that their work environment be raised to an equivalent level. Another justification for providing air-conditioned work areas is the fact that employees are more productive in comfortable environments.

In tests of production workers in air-conditioned space versus non-air-conditioned space, it was found that cool but stagnant atmosphere reduced output of the test group by nine percent. Warm atmosphere with air movement reduced output by 15 percent. Warm atmosphere with stagnant air reduced output by 23 percent and warm air with high humidity reduced output by 28 percent.[8]

PRODUCTIVITY

The installation of an enclosure for employees will generally have an influence on employees' work behavior and productivity. This influence may be favorable or adverse.

Physiologically, the removal of an employee from a noisy environment would lead to an improved performance of his job-related tasks. Task performance, or the ability to accomplish an assignment or requirement, is influenced by noise exposure. Tasks are assigned or self-imposed. The type and complexity of the task can vary from a simple mechanical or manual routine to the very imaginative or creative activity. The influence of noise is somewhat task dependent. Tasks, such as mechanical assembly, that require low mental concentration are least influenced by noise. Although their output remains fairly constant, noise will affect manual workers by increasing errors and making it difficult to stay alert. For low-order, manual, or mentally repetitious tasks, 90 dB is the recognized threshold for effective performance. There are currently no criteria for high-order mental tasks, but it is generally agreed that such activities are more vulnerable to noise exposure.

Psychologically, employee attitudes may be expected to vary due to the comfort and isolation provided by an enclosure.

Production problems are often feared by management when employee enclosures are considered. Employees may tend to get lazy, spend excessive time within the enclosure and neglect their operations. In most enclosure applications, the improved morale associated with the improved environment associated with the enclosure has shown to result in favorable rather than adverse production influences. Where problems have occurred, in many cases they may be traced to employee attitudinal problems which existed prior to the enclosure installation.

To minimize potential productivity problems associated with employee enclosures, the following remedies may be considered:

1. An employee relations program may be implemented.

2. Incentives may be increased for production quality and quantity.

3. The relative desirability of the enclosure with respect to the exterior work spaces may be minimized either by improving the exterior environment or diminishing the desirability of the enclosure (provide only ventilation rather than air-conditioning, etc.).

4. A partial enclosure or barrier may be installed rather than a comfortable enclosure.

5. The modified operation with an enclosure should receive special industrial engineering review. Different production procedures may be more applicable when an operation is controlled from a book, such as the installation of monitoring systems and other measures to reduce requirements for man-machine interactions.

SAFETY

Acoustical enclosures inherently provide considerable potential for employee safety; however, improper design may also lead to safety hazards which may not be present without an enclosure system.

Safety features are associated with the installation of an employee enclosure due to the fact that the employee is physically isolated from the industrial operations. Additional accident reduction potential is achieved when an enclosure reduces physical fatigue, improves operator mental awareness, or provides better operational control. Safety hazards may be created by enclosures due to the following:

1. An enclosure may provide a false sense of security and the employee may resort to the enclosure for protection from hazards for which it was not de-

signed to withstand. An example would be booths in a steel mill which may not withstand the impact of cobbles (hot steel bars which escape from conveyors).

2.   Normal safety precautions may be overlooked when they involve employees within enclosures. For example, crane operators may unconsciously pass loads over an employee located within an enclosure, while they would be less likely to do so if the employee's location was visible.

3.   An employee located in an enclosure may neglect an operation, and a hazard may occur or go undetected.

4.   When employees are isolated, they may not be aware if a co-worker is injured.

5.   Employees could become trapped within an enclosure in case of fire if adequate means for fire detection and enclosure exiting are not employed.

AIR QUALITY

Personnel enclosures may serve to isolate employees from adverse dust, fume, and gas environments by removing the employee from a potentially hazardous environment. The following five materials have been initially identified as target health hazards by the Occupational Safety and Health Act:

Asbestos
Cotton dust
Carbon monoxide
Lead
Silica

A summary of the human effects and current OSHA limits for these five materials is presented in Table 5.4.

Isolation of an employee by an enclosure may provide a near perfect improvement in air quality providing that adequate ventilation is provided utilizing either fresh or filtered air.

Table 5.4
Summary of five target health hazards

Material	Nature of Hazard	OSHA Limits
ASBESTOS (Dust)	Prolonged inhalation of asbestos fibers between 5 and 50 microns long can produce asbestosis, and possibly lung cancer.	Five fibers per milliliter greater than 5 microns in length for an 8-hour, time-weighted average air-borne concentration.
COTTON DUST (Dust)	Prolonged exposure can cause byssinosis, which can progress to chronic bronchitis and emphysema.	One milligram per cubic meter of air for an 8-hour, time-weighted average air-borne concentration.
CARBON MONOXIDE (Gas)	Carbon monoxide displaces oxygen in the blood, causing suffocation. High concentrations are fatal.	50 parts per million parts of air for 8-hour, time-weighted average air-borne concentration.
LEAD (Fume or Dust)	Prolonged exposure can cause severe gastrointestinal, blood, and central nervous system disorders.	0.2 milligrams per cubic meter of air for 8-hour, time-weighted average air-borne concentrations.
SILICA (Dust)	Excessive exposure can produce silicosis, a disabling lung disease.	For respirable quartz, 10 milligrams per cubic meter of air, divided by percent of free silica plus 2. For respirable cristobalite and tridymite, the limits are one-half the value of quartz.

HEAT STRESS

Exposure to excessive environmental temperatures may cause the following symptoms in humans:

Heat stroke
Heat hyperpyrexia
Heat exhaustion
Heat cramp
Heat rash

The promulgation of a heat stress regulation has been considered by OSHA for several years, and has been the subject of considerable research by NIOSH. While the controversey over the need for a heat stress regulation continues, few people doubt the inevitability of such a regulation.

The most recognized heat stress criteria is that adopted by the American Conference of Industrial Hygienists, as presented in Table 5.5.

Table 5.5
Threshold limit values for heat stress[9]

These Threshold Limit Values refer to heat stress conditions under which it is believed that nearly all workers may be repeatedly exposed without adverse health effects. The TLVs shown in Table 1 are based on the assumption that nearly all acclimatized, fully-clothed workers with adequate water and salt intake should be able to function effectively under the given working conditions without exceeding a deep body temperature of 38 C (WHO technical report series No. 412, 1969 *Health Factors Involved in Working Under Conditions of Heat Stress*).

Since measurement of deep body temperature is impractical for monitoring the workers' heat load, the measurement of environmental factors is required which most nearly correlate with deep body temperature and other physiological responses to heat. At the present time, Wet Bulb-Globe Temperature Index (WBGT) is the simplest and most suitable technique to measure the environmental factors. WBGT values are calculated by the following equations:

1. Outdoors with solar load:
   $$WBGT = 0.7WB + 0.2GT + 0.1DB$$

2. Indoors or Outdoors with no solar load:
   $$WBGT = 0.7WB + 0.3GT$$

where:

WBGT = Wet-Bulb-Globe Temperature Index
WB = Natural Wet-Bulb Temperature
DB = Dry-Bulb Temperature
GT = Globe Thermometer Temperature

The determination of WBGT requires the use of a black globe thermometer, a natural (static) wet-bulb thermometer, and a dry-bulb thermometer.

Table 5.5 continued

TABLE 1
PERMISSIBLE HEAT EXPOSURE
THRESHOLD LIMIT VALUES
(Values are given in°C, WBGT)

Work–Rest Regimen	Work Load		
	Light	*Moderate*	*Heavy*
Continuous work	30.0	26.7	25.0
75% Work– 25% Rest, Each hour	30.6	28.0	25.9
50% Work– 50% Rest, Each hour	31.4	29.4	27.9
25% Work– 75% Rest, Each hour	32.2	31.1	30.0

Higher heat exposures than shown in Table 1 are permissible if the workers have been undergoing medical surveillance and it has been established that they are more tolerant to work in heat than the average worker. Workers should not be permitted to continue their work when their deep body temperature exceeds 38.0 C.

APPENDIX

1. Measurement of the environment

The instruments required are a dry-bulb, a natural wet-bulb, a globe thermometer, and a stand. The measurement of the environmental factors shall be performed as follows:

A. The range of the dry and the natural wet bulb thermometer shall be −50 C to 50 C with an accuracy of ± 0.5 C. The dry bulb thermometer must be shielded from the sun and the other radiant surfaces of the environment without restricting the airflow around the bulb. The wick of the natural wet-bulb thermometer shall be kept wet with distilled water for at least ½ hour before the temperature reading is made. It is not enough to immerse the other end of the wick into a reservoir of distilled water and wait until the whole wick becomes wet by capillarity. The wick shall be wetted by direct application of water from a syringe ½ hour before each reading. The wick shall extend over the bulb of the thermometer, covering the stem about one additional bulb length. The wick should always be clean and new wicks should be washed before using.

/more/

Table 5.5 continued

B. One globe thermometer, consisting of a 15 cm. (6-inch) diameter hollow copper sphere, painted on the outside with a matte black finish or equivalent shall be used. The bulb or sensor of a thermometer (range −5 C to 100 C with an accuracy of ± 0.5 C) must be fixed in the center of the sphere. The globe thermometer shall be exposed at least 25 minutes before it is read.

C. One stand shall be used to suspend the three thermometers so that they do not restrict free air flow around the bulbs, and the wet bulb and globe thermometer are not shaded.

D. It is permissible to use any other type of temperature sensor that gives identical reading to a mercury thermometer under the same conditions.

E. The thermometers must be so placed that the readings are representative of the condition where the men work or rest, respectively.

The methodology outlined above is more fully explained in the following publications:

1. "Prevention of Heat Casualties in Marine Corps Recruits, 1955−1960, with Comparative Incidence Rates and Climatic Heat Stresses in other Training Categories," by Captain David Minard, MC, USN, Research Report No. 4, Contract No. MR005.01−0001.01, Naval Medical Research Institute, Bethesda, Maryland, 21 February 1961.

2. "Heat Casualties in the Navy and Marine Corps, 1959−1962, with Appendices on the Field Use of the Wet Bulb-Globe Temperature Index," by Captain David Minard, MC, USN, and R. L. O'Brien, HMC, USN. Research Report No. 7, Contract No. MR 005.01−0001.01, Naval Medical Research Institute, Bethesda, Maryland, 12 March 1964.

3. Minard, D.: Prevention of Heat Casualties in Marine Corps Recruits. Military Medicine 126 (4): 261−272, 1961.

II. Work load categories

The heat produced by the body and the environmental heat together determine the total heat load. Therefore, if work is to be performed under hot environmental conditions, the workload category of each job shall be established and the heat exposure limit pertinent to the work load evaluated against the applicable standard in order to protect the worker from exposure beyond the permissible limit.

A. The work load category may be established by ranking each job into light, medium, and heavy categories on the basis of type of operation, where the work load is ranked into one of said three categories, i.e.

(1) light work: e.g., sitting or standing to control machines, performing light hand or arm work.

(2) moderate work: e.g., walking about with moderate lifting and pushing.

(3) heavy work: e.g., pick and shovel work,

the permissible heat exposure limit for that work load shall be determined from Table 1.

Table 5.5 continued

B. The ranking of the job may be performed either by measuring the worker's metabolic rate while performing his job or by estimating his metabolic rate by the use of the scheme shown in Table 2. Tables available in the literature listed below and in other publications as well may also be utilized.

1. Per-Olaf Astrand and Kaare Rodahl: "Textbook of Work Physiology," McGraw-Hill Book Company, New York, San Francisco, 1970.

2. Ergonomics Guide to Assessment of Metabolic and Cardiac Costs of Physical Work. Amer. Ind. Hyg. Assoc. J. 32:560, 1971.

3. Energy Requirements for Physical Work. Purdue Farm Cardiac Project. Agricultural Experiment Station. Research Progress Report No. 30, 1961.

4. J. V. G. A. Durnin and R. Passmore: "Energy, Work and Leisure." Heinemann Educational Books, Ltd., London, 1967.

TABLE 2
ASSESSMENT OF WORK LOAD

Average values of metabolic rate during different activities.

A. Body position and movement			Kcal./min.
Sitting			0.3
Standing			0.6
Walking			2.0–3.0
Walking up hill			add 0.8
			per meter (yard) rise

B. Type of Work		Average Kcal./min.	Range Kcal./min.
Hand work			
	light	0.4	0.2–1.2
	heavy	0.9	
Work with one arm			
	light	1.0	0.7–2.5
	heavy	1.8	
Work with both arms			
	light	1.5	1.0–3.5
	heavy	2.5	
Work with body			
	light	3.5	2.5–15.0
	moderate	5.0	
	heavy	7.0	
	very heavy	9.0	

Light hand work: writing, hand knitting
Heavy hand work: typewriting

/more/

Table 5.5 continued

Heavy work with one arm: hammering in nails (shoemaker, upholsterer)
Light work with two arms: filing metal, planing wood, raking of a garden
Moderate work with the body: cleaning a floor, beating a carpet
Heavy work with the body: railroad track laying, digging, barking trees

Sample Calculation: Using a heavy hand tool on an assembly line

A. Walking along   2.0 Kcal./min.

B. Intermediate value between heavy work with
    two arms and light work with the body   3.0 Kcal./min.

     5.0 Kcal./min.

C. Add for basal metabolism   1.0 Kcal./min.

      Total   6.0 Kcal./min.

Adapted from Lehmann, G. E., A. Muller and H. Spitzer: Der Kalorienbedarf bei gewerblicher Arbeit. Arbeitsphysiol. 14: 166, 1950.

III.   Work-rest regimen

The permissible exposure limits specified in Table I and Diagram A are based on the assumption that the WBGT value of the resting place is the same or very close to that of the work place. If the resting place is air-conditioned and its climate is kept at or below 24 C (75 F), WBGT, the allowable resting time may be reduced by 25%. The permissible exposure limits for continuous work are applicable where there is a work-rest regimen of a 5-day work week and an 8-hour work day with a short morning and afternoon break (approximately 15 minutes) and a longer lunch break (approximately 30 minutes). Higher exposure limits are permitted if additional resting time is allowed. All breaks, including unscheduled pauses and administrative or operational waiting periods during work may be counted as rest time when additional rest allowance must be given because of high environmental temperatures.

It is a common experience that when the work on a job is self-paced, the workers will spontaneously limit their hourly work load to 30–50 percent of their maximum physical performance capacity. They do this either by setting an appropriate work speed or by interspersing unscheduled breaks. Thus the daily average of the workers' metabolic rate seldom exceeds 330 kcal/hr. However, within an 8-hour work shift there may be periods where the workers' hourly average metabolic rate will be higher.

IV.   Water and salt supplementation

During the hot season or when the worker is exposed to artificially generated heat, drinking water shall be made available to the workers in such a way that they are stimulated to frequently drink small amounts, i.e., one cup every 15–20 minutes (about 150 ml or ¼ pint).

The water shall be kept reasonably cool (10–15 C or 50.0–60.0 F) and shall be placed close to the workplace so that the worker can reach it without abandoning the work area.

Table 5.5 concluded

The workers should be encouraged to salt their food abundantly during the hot season and particularly during hot spells. If the workers are unacclimatized, salted drinking water shall be made available in a concentration of 0.1 percent (lg NaCl to 1.0 liter or 1 level tablespoon of salt to 15 quarts of water). The added salt shall be completely dissolved before the water is distributed, and the water shall be kept reasonably cool.

V. Other considerations

A. Clothing: The permissible heat exposure TLVs are valid for light summer clothing as customarily worn by workers when working under hot environmental conditions. If special clothing is required for performing a particular job and this clothing is heavier or it impedes sweat evaporation or has higher insulation value, the worker's heat tolerance is reduced and the permissible heat exposure limits indicated in Table 1 and Figure 1 are not applicable. For each job category where special clothing is required, the permissible heat exposure limit shall be established by an expert.

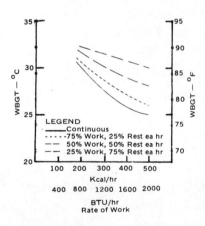

FIG. 1–Permissible Heat Exposure Threshold Limit Value

B. Acclimatization and Fitness: The recommended heat stress TLVs are valid for acclimated workers who are physically fit.

Ionizing Radiation

See U.S. Department of Commerce National Bureau of Standards, Handbook 59, "Permissible Dose from External Sources of Ionizing Radiation," September 24, 1954, and addendum of April 15, 1958. A report, Basic Radiation Protection Criteria, published by the National Committee on Radiation Protection, revises and modernizes the concept of the NCRP standards of 1954, 1957 and 1958; obtainable as NCRP Rept. No. 39, P.O. Box 4867, Washington, D.C. 20008.

PHYSICAL AGENTS

In addition to isolation from adverse noise, air, and heat environments, enclosures may serve to protect employees from the following physical agents: ionizing radiation, cold, sunlight, humidity, X-rays, water, lasers, poisons, microwaves, ultraviolet radiation, and electricity.

REFERENCES

1. Fitzroy, J., "Reverberation Formula Which Seems to be More Accurate with Nonuniform Distribution Absorption," *Journal Acoustical American Society,* Vol. XXXI, No. 7, July 1959, p. 893.
2. Bolt, Beranek, and Newman, Inc., *Noise Control for Reciprocating and Turbine Engines Driven by Natural Gas and Liquid Fuel,* American Gas Association, 1969.
3. Jokel, C. R., "Statistical Analysis of Noise Exposure—A Worthwhile Technique?", Proceedings of NOISEXPO 76, New York, 29—31 March 1976, pp 73—77.
4. Miller, T. D., and Fader, B., "Economical Noise Control," Proceedings of NOISEXPO 76, New York, 29—31 March 1976, pp 97—100.
5. Yerges, L. F., "Control the Noise—or the Exposure?", NOISEXPO 77, Chicago, 14—17 March 1977.
6. Colliton, T. J., "Evaluation of Noise Dose as a Function of Task Routine," *Sound and Vibration,* Vol. 9, No. 5, May 1975, pp 32—34.
7. Doelle, L., *Environmental Acoustics,* McGraw-Hill, 1972.
8. Spector, L. (ed), *Plant Engineering Directory and Specification Catalog,* Technical Publishing Company, 1976.
9. American Conference of Governmental Industrial Hygienists, 1973.

6

Analysis and Design Procedures for Machine Enclosures

The isolation of noise producing machinery by means of acoustical enclosures provides the greatest noise reduction potential of all approaches which may be taken to equipment noise abatement. Noise reductions of 20–30 dBA are common with machine enclosures, and with special isolation treatment, noise reductions above 50 dBA may be achieved. Generally, there are no inherent disadvantages in machine enclosure, other than the initial cost of the installation, if employee accessibility is not required. If accessibility is required, such as in the case of manually operated machinery, enclosures may cause problems ranging in severity from hampered production to total lack of feasibility. Often clever design approaches may minimize these potential problems.

The proper design of a machine enclosure requires the correct application of basic engineering principles. All too often, the noise control attitude taken toward enclosure design is "build a box around the machine." Production and operational problems inevitably and appropriately arise when this lack of engineering concern for enclosure design is taken. This chapter will discuss the engineering fundamentals which should be considered in enclosure design, including the following:

1. Design guidelines for acoustical effectiveness
2. Consideration of machine operational requirements
3. Insuring production compatibility
4. Maintaining employee safety and welfare

It is often thought that the insulation of an enclosure for a machine can only hamper the machine operation and restrict accessibility; thus the typical design attitude is to minimize the negative aspects of the design. This fundamental prejudice against enclosures has undoubtedly resulted in the failure of hundreds of installations to achieve the potential advantages which clever engineering could have achieved.

It is not by accident that the design of contemporary office equipment, including typewriters and copy machines, is centered around the enclosure of the machinery mechanisms. This trend is being followed in the design of many current generation models of industrial equipment,[1] for reasons other than noise reduction. The advantages of machine shrouds include: aesthetics, safety, oil mist control, energy conservation, reduction of employee tampering, containment of machine-emitted air contaminants, and cost savings.

ENCLOSURE TYPES

Three design approaches may be considered for machine enclosures, depending upon machine operational requirements and the extent of noise reduction required. These are:

1. Localized enclosure
2. Partial enclosure
3. Complete enclosure

LOCALIZED ENCLOSURES

In many machines, high noise levels are associated with only localized machine elements. Where isolated noise sources are identified on a machine, it may be more efficient to enclose only a small area, rather than the entire machine.

For complex machines, it is not always evident which machine elements are radiating excessive noise levels. Noise producing components may be identified by measuring vibration levels and calculating the expected sound levels from the machine element in question. The near-field sound pressure levels due to panel vibration may be calculated above the panel coincidence frequency from:

$$L_p = L_v - 20 \log f + 150 \qquad (6\text{-}1)$$

where: L_p = sound pressure level, dB re .0002 microbar

L_v = vibration level, dB re 1.0 g

f = frequency, Hz

The coincidence frequency can be calculated as presented in Chapter 4, Equation (4-2).

Below the coincidence frequency, the panel sound radiation will be 3–4 dB/octave less than predicted by Equation (6-1). Equation (6-1) is valid only for frequencies with wavelengths less than the panel dimension.

High levels of vibration are generally characteristic of noise producing machinery, and it is not an uncommon phenomenon for vibrations to be transmitted from a machine to an acoustical enclosure. These vibrations cause the enclosure itself to become a noise source, and partially negate noise reduction potential. In a general machine system, heavy structural elements serve to transmit vibration to lightweight surfaces which are prime sound radiators. Thus a lightweight enclosure attached directly to a machine with high vibration may radiate higher noise levels than the machine without an enclosure.

As a general guideline, acoustical enclosure panels should never be attached directly to machine elements which have high vibration levels. Where panels are machine mounted, vibration isolation techniques should be employed as shown in Figure 6.1. To insure minimum sound radiation due to panel vibration, vibration damping treatment should also be applied to machine-mounted enclosures.

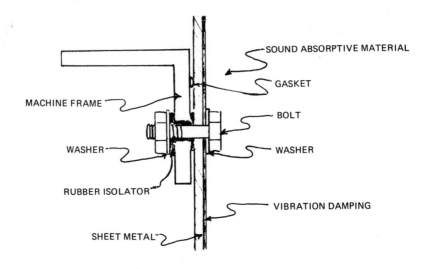

**Figure 6.1. Technique for vibration isolation of
enclosure panel from machine frame**

PARTIAL ENCLOSURES

A machine enclosure which has at least one open side or a very
large opening may be considered as a partial enclosure.

A partial machine enclosure will provide virtually no noise
reduction for an employee working directly at the machine unless it:

a.   Interrupts the line-of-sight path between the machine
and the operator's hearing zone, or

b.   Absorbs sound which is reflected from the machine
to the operator by an adjacent wall or ceiling.

A partial machine enclosure will generally not be effective
if the interior surfaces are not sound absorptive. Acoustically reflective surfaces will serve to focus sound out the opening of a
partial enclosure and will generally increase the operator's noise

exposure. A partial enclosure with a nonabsorptive interior may reduce the noise exposure for employees in the direct vicinity of the enclosure whose line-of-sight path to the noise source is interrupted. However, the enclosure would not provide any reduction in the overall sound levels of the workspace, since the acoustical energy emanating from the machine into the workspace would not be reduced, but only redirected.

The noise reduction provided by a partial enclosure with sound absorptive interior, as measured in the reverberant field of the machine, will be proportional to the percentage of the machine which is enclosed ($NR \leq TL-3$):

$$NR = IL = 10 \log \frac{1}{1 - \%A} \qquad (6\text{-}2)$$

where:　NR = Noise reduction, dB

　　　　IL = Insertion loss, dB

　　　　$\%A$ = Percent of enclosed area, expressed as a decimal

Thus, the noise reduction provided by a square, three-sided enclosure without a top or front side would be:

$$NR = 10 \log \left(\frac{1}{1 - .66} \right) = 4.8 \text{ dB}$$

COMPLETE ENCLOSURES

Complete machine enclosures may be classified into three types:

1. Noise source in a building
2. Large enclosure
3. Closely-fitting enclosure

The noise reduction for each of these three types is considered separately.

The basic analysis of sound transmission loss, sound absorption, and acoustical walls, as presented in Chapters 2 and 4, apply directly to machine enclosures.

Large Enclosures[2] —A fairly diffuse reverberant sound field exists within the air space between a noise source and an enclosure when the noise source is small compared to the total enclosure volume (generally less than one-third). For machine enclosures of this type:

$$NR = TL \qquad\qquad (6\text{-}3)$$

and,

$$IL = TL - 10 \log\left(\frac{1}{\alpha}\right) \qquad\qquad (6\text{-}4)$$

where: NR = noise reduction due to enclosure, dB

IL = insertion loss due to enclosure, dB

TL = sound transmission loss of enclosure wall, dB

α = average sound absorption coefficient of interior of enclosure.

From Equation (6-4), the importance of sound absorption inside a machine enclosure is recognized. If the sound absorption coefficient is only 0.1, the insertion loss will be reduced by 10 dB. As the sound absorption coefficient approaches unity, the insertion loss becomes equal to the sound transmission loss.

Closely-Fitting Enclosures[2] —The theory for large enclosures is not valid if the noise source nearly fills the enclosure. This occurs, for example, when the enclosure takes the form of a closely-fitting hood. The most significant published research on closely-fitting enclosures is found in two papers by Jackson[3,4] and is further reported by King[5] and Beranek.[6] The basic idea is that with closely-fitting enclosures on mechanical machinery, the enclosure structure and machinery inside must be considered as dynamically coupled vibrating systems. As a result the enclosure can greatly modify the amount of sound power radiated by the noise source inside. This is in sharp contrast to the large enclosure and partition situations where the sound power output of the noise source is considered independent of the large space in which it is placed.

With a closely-fitting enclosure there is a sequence of resonance frequencies at which the insertion loss performance of the enclosure may be severely reduced, i.e., compared to the Mass Law. These "window" frequencies are associated with two systems of resonances. Firstly, there are the panel resonances of the enclosure structure. If the enclosure panel structure is lightly damped the insertion loss of the enclosure will usually become **negative** at these panel resonances. In other words, the enclosure may radiate more sound power than the machinery inside would bare. The enclosure is then acting as a resonant sounding board. The two design approaches for minimizing the problem near panel resonances are:

1. Provide structural damping.

2. Keep panel resonances away from frequencies that require a high insertion loss.

The other frequencies at which the insertion loss may be sharply reduced are associated with standing wave resonances in the air space between the enclosure and the noise source. In the typical case where the machinery inside has a flat surface parallel to the enclosure these standing wave resonances are easily predicted to be at frequencies when the air gap measures an integer number of half-wavelengths. The n'th order resonance in terms of L measured in inches is:

$$f_n = (6700/L)n \, , \, n = 1, 2, 3, \ldots \qquad (6\text{-}5)$$

Fortunately, the remedy for decrease in insertion loss at these standing wave resonances is generally straightforward: sound absorptive material on the inside of the enclosure. Typical porous materials with a rigid backing become effective absorbers only when they measure at least a quarter wavelength thick. Thus, to damp out all air resonances including the lowest, the layer of absorptive material should be about half the thickness of the air space.

OPENING IN AN ENCLOSURE

The sound power level that passes through an opening into or out of a room may be calculated from:

$$L_w = L_p + 10 \log S - 10.5 \qquad (6\text{-}6)$$

where: L_w =   sound power level passing through opening, dB re 10^{-12} watt

L_p =   sound pressure level in room, dB re .0002 microbar

S =   surface area of opening, square feet

To insure the effectiveness of an acoustical enclosure, openings should be prevented or minimized. Where openings are necessary, such as for ventilation, silencers or "sound traps" should be installed (refer to Chapter 8).

VIBRATION ISOLATION

Vibrations may be transmitted through the floor to enclosures. The large surface area enclosure panels may become a noise source. This problem may be avoided by the mounting of the machine on vibration isolators. The typical vibration levels of a bolted and isolated blanking press, shown in Table 6.1, indicate the effectiveness of vibration isolation.[8]

Guidelines for vibration isolation are presented in reference 7.

NONACOUSTICAL REQUIREMENTS

In addition to the design of an acoustical enclosure to meet noise reduction objectives, the following additional design requirements should be considered:

Table 6.1
Linear vibration levels in decibels re 1.0 g
for 250-ton blanking press[8]

Structural Measurement Location	Press Bolted	Press Isolated
Press Leg	+ 22	+ 7
Foundation	−3	−30
Floor	−21	−41
Building Column	−10	−25

1. Visibility should be provided.

2. The enclosure should be properly ventilated to prevent heat build-up.

3. Operational accessibility should be provided to meet production requirements.

4. Localized and complete accessibility should be provided for maintenance.

5. If audible signals are utilized to assess machine performance alternate detection systems should be installed.

6. Supply systems must be provided to the enclosed machinery to meet energy and process requirements.

7. In-feed and out-feed openings should be designed which provide noise attenuation consistent with the total enclosure system but which will not impede material flow.

8. An internal lighting system should be installed if the enclosure shadows exterior lighting excessively.

9. Protection should be provided against employee and vehicular (lift trucks, etc.) damage.

10. Protection should be provided against operational abuse: moisture, water spray, oil, grease, dirt, erosion by fluid flow, etc.

11.   In food process plants, materials should not be damaged by cleaning or disinfecting. Materials which may be in contact with food must meet FDA requirements. Uninspected spaces in which vermin may hide should be eliminated.

12.   Flame-spread and fire-endurance limits should be specified for all materials. Firebreak requirements should be employed on all ducts, pipe runs, and shafts. Smoke or temperature alarms may also be considered for enclosures.

13.   Safety requirements should be observed.

14.   The enclosure should be aesthetically compatible with the surrounding environment.

15.   Security systems may be installed in conjunction with the enclosure system to prevent employee tampering.

Detailed design guidelines related to many of these requirements are presented throughout this book. Material requirements as related to fire-resistance codes, food-processing plants and high-temperature environments were covered in Chapter 3. In Chapter 5, design guidelines for visibility, productivity, safety, and protection from physical agents were discussed. Enclosure ventilation requirements are analyzed in Chapter 8.

Supplementing this information, the following sections discuss design approaches related to auditory detection, safety and openings for material flow and access.

AUDITORY DETECTION

If auditory detection is mandatory for an operation, the approach is dependent upon the noise reduction required. It must also be recognized that a sound level reduction will not necessarily impede audibility. For example, a person can generally hear better with hearing protective devices than without because:

1.   sound levels which mask a signal to be heard are also attenuated, and

2.   the effect of a temporary threshold shift is reduced.

In the case of enclosures, however, the transmission loss frequency characteristics will distort the sound. Enclosures which provide a large noise reduction (20–40 dB) can cause severe detection interference. In this case, machine noise is generally not detected but usually openings for material flow allow some sound to escape the enclosure and signal audibility may be maintained.

Another approach to the problem is to install a control system of warning lights to replace audible warnings. A final solution may be to install a sound reinforcement system with microphone pickups positioned near critical machine elements to detect audible system characteristics and to transmit the sounds electronically to a loudspeaker within the enclosure. Such a system may also be coupled with a closed-circuit television monitoring system. While these approaches may appear elaborate as noise control measures, these modifications may result in substantial direct cost savings or production benefits due to increased process control and decreased manpower requirements.

SAFETY

Acoustical machine enclosures, if properly designed, may serve as excellent machine guards. Special design considerations must be made, however, if an enclosure is also to serve as a guard. In addition, the designer should insure that the enclosure does not become a safety problem, such as where safety glass is not used, the enclosure is not structurally sound, etc.

The proper design of an enclosure must go beyond the simple elimination of unsafe design features, but must also be designed to minimize accident risks due to employee carelessness or negligence. It was recognized by Heinrich[9] as far back as 1931, that 88 percent of all accidents result primarily from unsafe acts, 10 percent from unsafe conditions, and 2 percent from "acts of God" or unpreventable circumstances. Thus,

machine enclosures should employ devices such as interlock systems to shut off a machine when the enclosure is opened.

OPENINGS FOR ACCESS,
MATERIAL FLOW,
AND AIR FLOW

An operation within an enclosure cannot function as a closed
system if it is to serve a useful function. Material flow and/or
energy transfer into and out of the enclosure are necessary.
Often access by operators and ventilation are also required.
These functions require openings in the enclosure which must
be acoustically treated if the enclosure's noise reduction potential is not to be compromised.

Several acoustical designs may be considered to reduce
sound levels emanating from an enclosure opening:

1.   Straight lined ducts
2.   Lined ducts with 90° bend
3.   Lined ducts with 180° bend
4.   Labyrinth paths

The Sabine formula may be used to estimate the attenuation of a lined duct:[10]

$$A = 12.6 \ \frac{P}{A} \ \alpha^{1.4} \qquad\qquad (6\text{-}7)$$

where: A =   attenuation per lineal foot, dB

P =   duct perimeter, inches

A =   cross-sectional area of duct, square inches

α =   sound absorption coefficient of lining

This formula only holds true for a relatively low range of frequencies (i.e. 250 Hz to 2000 Hz) and becomes increasingly in-
accurate as the ratio of duct length to wavelength increases. It
is also dependent on the value of α being between 0.2 and 0.4;
and the ratio on the major to minor dimension of a rectangular
duct being 1 and 2.

Wherever possible, actual duct data should be used. Figure 6.2 shows attenuation characteristics for a 16-inch duct with one- and two-inch lining.[11]

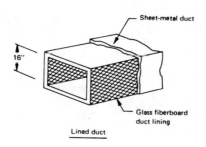

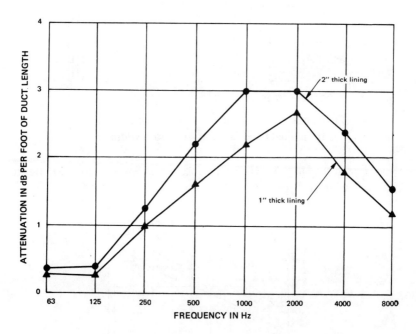

Figure 6.2. Acoustical duct attenuation[11]

The sound attenuation characteristics for a duct with a 90° lined bend are presented in Figure 6.3.[12] The sound absorption coefficient for the lining should be at least 0.8 for frequencies for which the ratio d/λ (duct diameter divided by wavelength) is greater than 1.5.

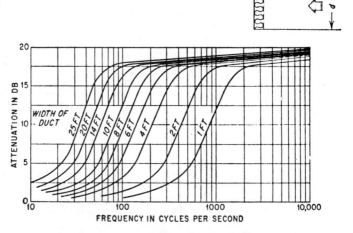

Figure 6.3. Attenuation as a function of frequency for a lined bend in ducts of various widths[12]

The sound attenuation characteristics for a lined 180° bend are presented in Figure 6.4.[13]

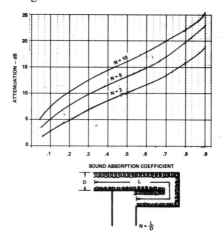

Figure 6.4. Attenuation by a 180° lined bend in a duct[13]

Sound transmission through openings required for material flow may also be attenuated by the installation of a double row of slitted curtains, as shown in Figure 6.5. The curtains should be fabricated of a soft rubber material, such as vinyl, to allow easy material passage, and the slits in the curtains should be staggered to minimize sound leakage.

TWO SHEETS OF VINYL, 1/8″ THICK,
WITH STAGGERED SLITS.
ANY FLEXIBLE PLASTIC OR RUBBER MATERIAL
MAY BE USED AS AN ALTERNATIVE, BUT MUST
BE A MINIMUM OF 1/8″ THICK.

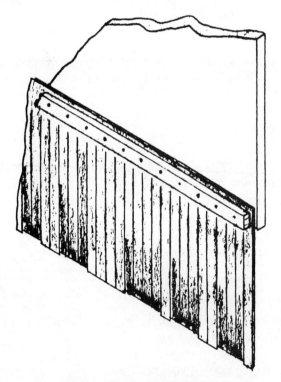

Figure 6.5. Acoustical curtain

Where large openings are required, lined bends may be installed to form labyrinth sound traps, as shown in Figure 6.6.

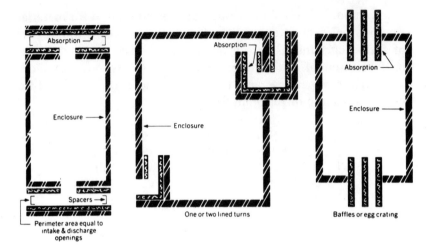

**Figure 6.6. Labyrinth sound traps for large openings
in enclosures** (courtesy The Soundcoat Company)

SPECIFICATION

Where acoustical enclosures are purchased from an outside contractor or vendor, each potential supplier should be provided with a specification which outlines both the acoustical and mechanical performance requirements for the enclosure. A typical specification format is illustrated below (courtesy of Environmental Elements Corporation):

GENERAL

The acoustical enclosure shall be constructed in accordance with the following paragraphs:

PANEL MATERIALS AND CONSTRUCTION

Panels shall be 2" nominal thickness, fabricated with a minimum 18 gauge galvanized steel back sheet, a minimum of 22 gauge galvanized perforated steel face sheet, and 16 gauge galvanized steel channel stiffeners and frames. Channel frames shall be provided on all four edges of the panels for structural integrity, and wrap-around back sheet construction will not be permitted. Perforations in the face sheet shall be 5/64" diameter on 5/32" staggered centers, or equivalent.

Panels shall be packed with nonabsorptive, vermin-proof, incombustible acoustical-thermal insulating material. This acoustical-thermal material shall be packed such that no settling will occur.

CONNECTIONS

All wall and ceiling panel connections are to be 16 gauge galvanized steel and shall connect all joints and corners such that no direct path occurs for sound leakage when properly installed. Connections shall be furnished undrilled in standard lengths for field cutting to required dimensions. Panel connectors and wall corners shall fit inside the panel frames and also fit inside connectors for a tight seal and the elimination of field coping and fitting.

DOORS

Access, single and/or double doors shall be provided in standard sizes where shown on the drawings. Doors shall have double seals and be equipped with strap hinges and double-action latches.

WINDOWS

Single pane safety glass or lexan shall be provided with a minimum thickness of ½". All windows shall be properly gasketed.

VENTILATION

A fan and system shall be included to provide a minimum of one air volume change per minute.

STRUCTURAL RIGIDITY

Panel shall be self-supporting under normal conditions up to a panel span of 10 ft. (For spans exceeding 10 ft. structural members or columns shall be supplied by erector.)

PERFORMANCE

Panels and doors shall be acoustical class 30 and shall have the following transmission loss characteristics without exception:

Hertz	125	250	500	1000	2000	4000
Decibels	10	15	25	35	35	35

Panels shall have the following minimum absorption coefficients without exception:

Hertz	125	250	500	1000	2000	4000
Absorption Coefficient	.25	.50	.75	.75	.75	.75

Acoustic class and transmission loss data shall be the results of tests in accordance with ASTM E-90-61T.

Absorption coefficients shall be the results of tests in accordance with the ASTM C-423-60T.

GUARANTEE

The panel manufacturer shall guarantee that all panels and components will adhere to the above specifications without exception and will be free from defects in materials and workmanship for a period of one (1) year from date of delivery.

FIRE RATING PERFORMANCE

a)   Flame Spread — not over 25.

b)   Fuel Contributed — not over 50.

c)   Smoke Developed — not over 50.

TYPICAL ENCLOSURE DESIGNS

Figures 6.7 through 6.28 demonstrate several enclosure designs which were recommended for noise control of various items of machinery. It will be noted that many of the enclosures involve only the localized enclosure of the noise generating elements of the machine rather than the entire machine. The enclosure designs employ windows and doors as necessary for production operation and maintenance.

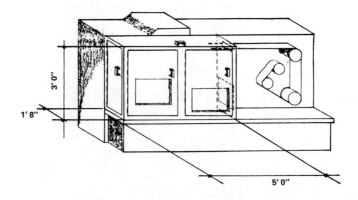

Figure 6.7. Enclosure for large tape printer

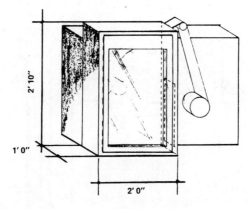

Figure 6.8. Enclosure for small tape printer

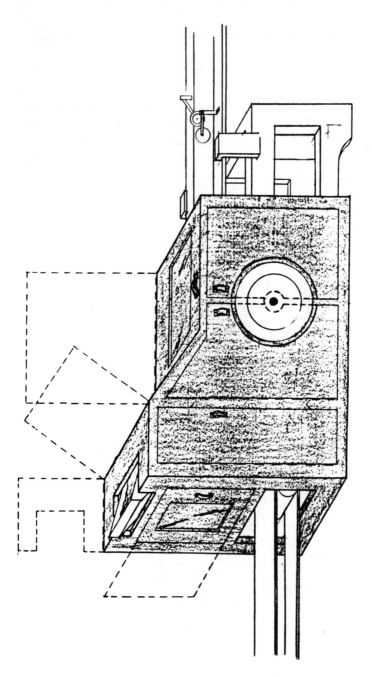

Figure 6.9. Complete acoustical enclosure for grocery bag machine

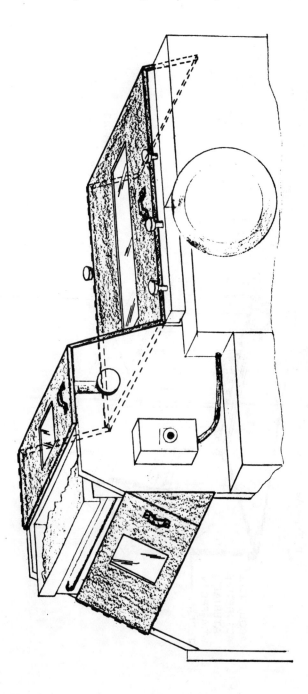

Figure 6.10. Partial acoustical enclosure for grocery bag machine

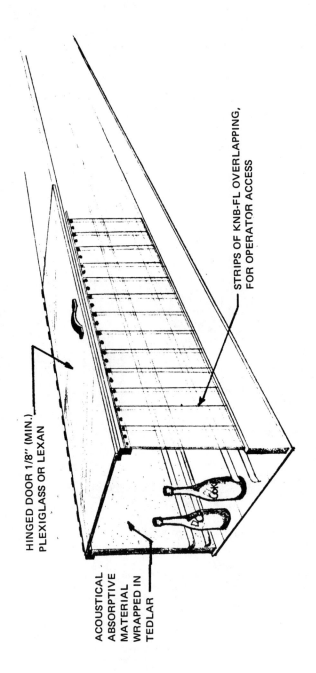

STRIPS OF KNB-FL OVERLAPPING, FOR OPERATOR ACCESS

HINGED DOOR 1/8" (MIN.) PLEXIGLASS OR LEXAN

ACOUSTICAL ABSORPTIVE MATERIAL WRAPPED IN TEDLAR

Figure 6.11. Acoustical enclosure for bottle conveyor line

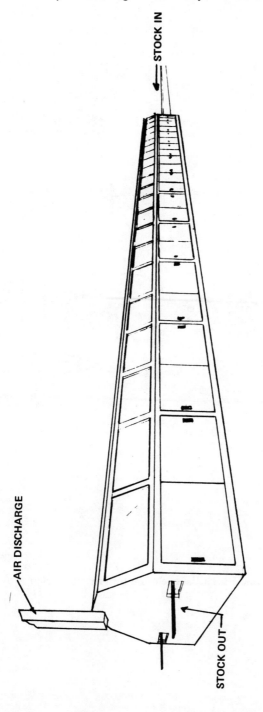

STOCK IN

AIR DISCHARGE

STOCK OUT

Figure 6.12: Acoustical enclosure for automated assembly line.
Rows of windows and doors permit visibility and access.

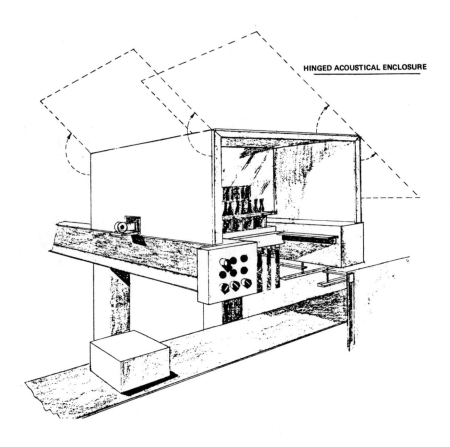

Figure 6.13. Partial enclosure for can case packer

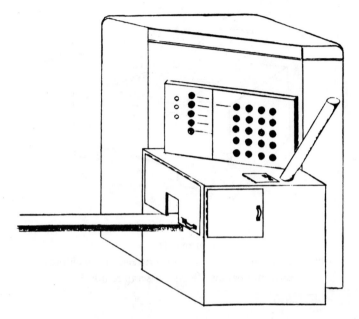

Figure 6.14. Acoustical enclosure for can seamer

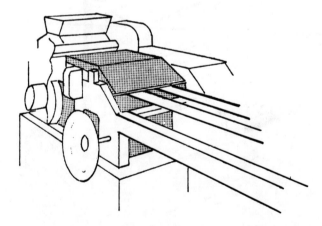

Figure 6.15

A localized acoustical enclosure for ice cream bag machine. The enclosed area included the paper cutting and folding operations. The enclosure featured a hinged and gasketed door on the top, clear plastic window, no openings to allow sound leaks, and an interior lining of a sound absorbing foam.

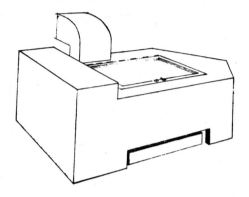

Figure 6.16
Acoustical enclosure for vibrator outfeed of punch press
Bottom opening allows for scrap removal

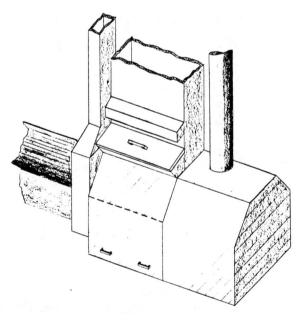

Figure 6.17
Enclosure for hammer mill, featuring modular panels of
glass fiber lined sheet metal

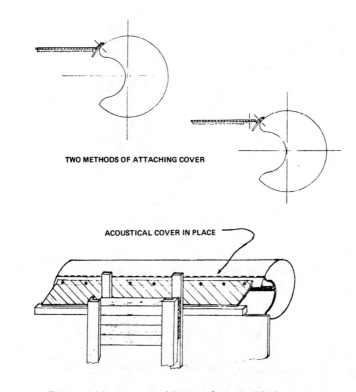

TWO METHODS OF ATTACHING COVER

ACOUSTICAL COVER IN PLACE

Figure 6.18. Acoustical barrier for wood lathe

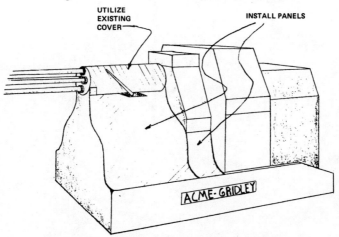

UTILIZE
EXISTING
COVER

INSTALL PANELS

ACME-GRIDLEY

Figure 6.19. Acoustical enclosure for screw machine

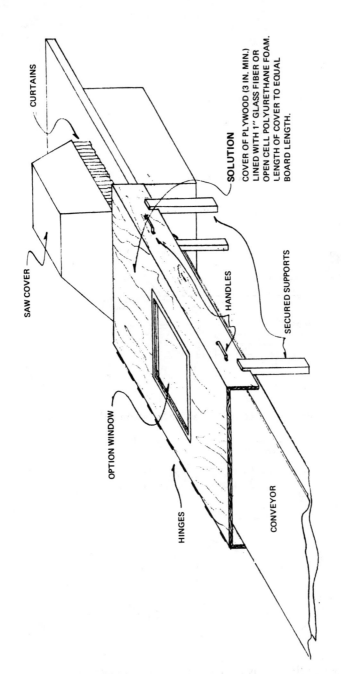

CURTAINS

SOLUTION

COVER OF PLYWOOD (3 IN. MIN.) LINED WITH 1" GLASS FIBER OR OPEN CELL POLYURETHANE FOAM. LENGTH OF COVER TO EQUAL BOARD LENGTH.

SAW COVER

HANDLES

SECURED SUPPORTS

OPTION WINDOW

HINGES

CONVEYOR

Figure 6.20. Outfeed cover for gang rip saw

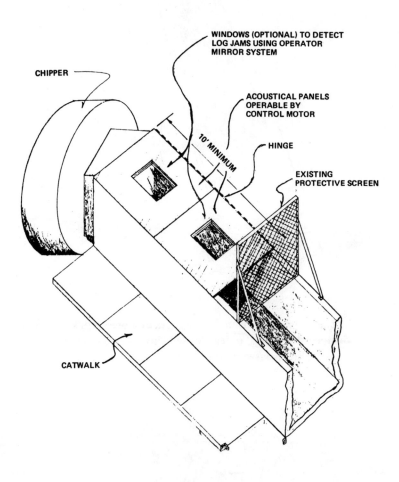

Figure 6.21. Inlet silencer for wood chipper

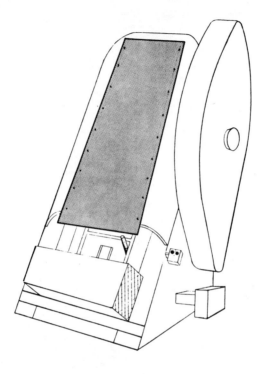

Figure 6.22. Localized enclosure for ram area of a press, constructed of damped sheet metal or lead-loaded vinyl. The die space is also enclosed with a clear plastic material.

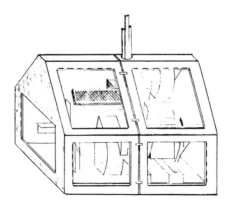

Figure 6.23. Acoustical enclosure for high speed automatic press The enclosure provides for both operator viewing of the operation and maintenance access

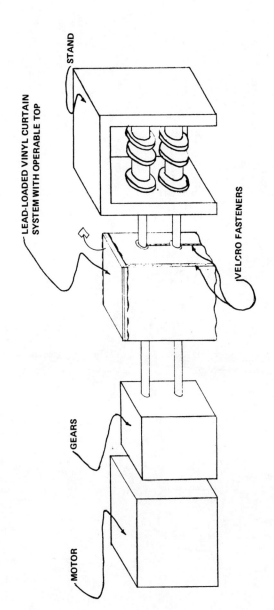

STAND

LEAD-LOADED VINYL CURTAIN SYSTEM WITH OPERABLE TOP

VELCRO FASTENERS

GEARS

MOTOR

Figure 6.24. Curtain acoustical enclosure for steel mill couplings

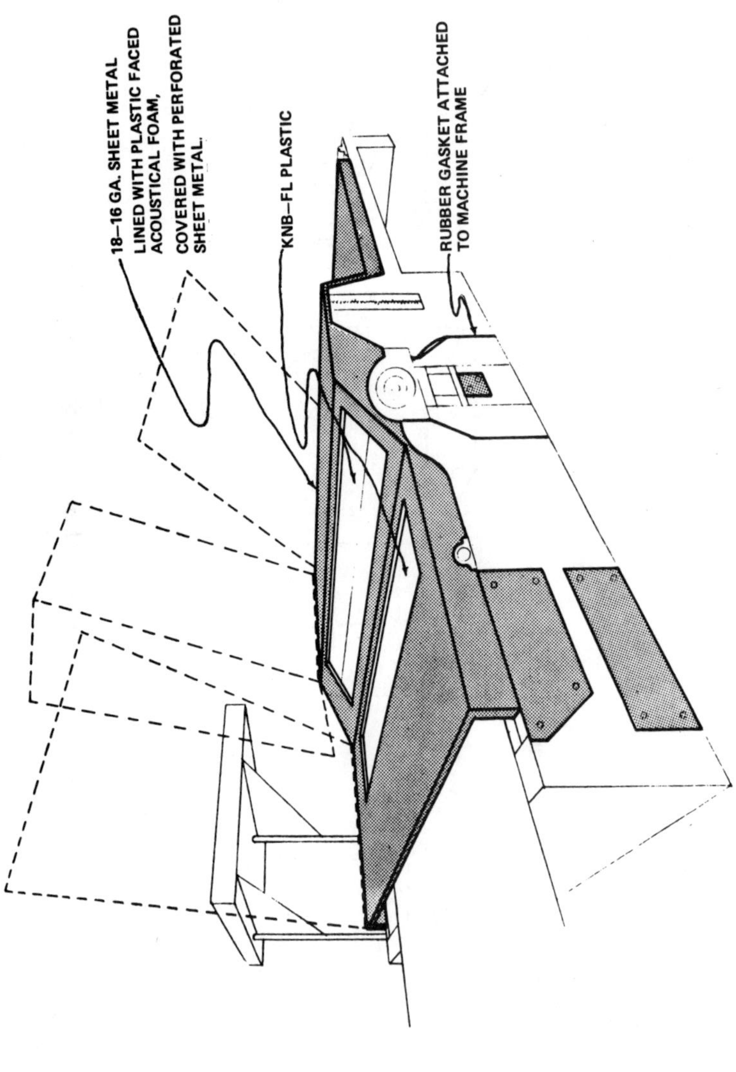

Figure 6.25. Acoustical enclosure for cutter. All enclosure panels are hinged for access.

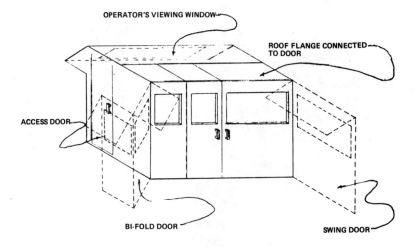

Figure 6.26
Acoustical enclosure with large doors for
material loading and complete machine access

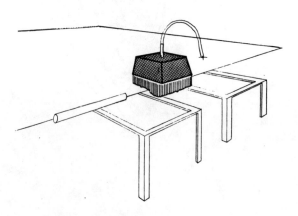

Figure 6.27
Localized enclosure for Vacu-blast abrasive sheet cleaner

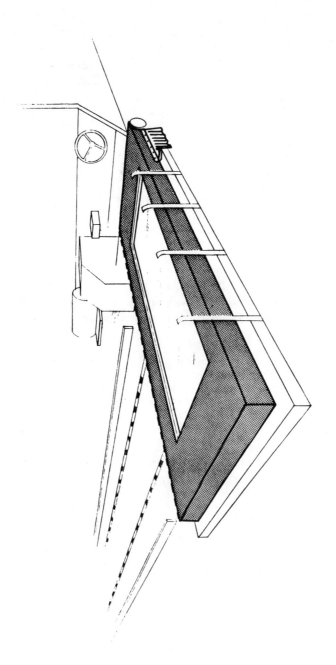

Figure 6.28. Localized enclosure for sheet metal impact point on automatic conveyor

REFERENCES

1. Knapp, J. G., "Industrial Design, Its Role in Cost Reduction," *Mechanical Engineering,* V 93, no. 12, December 1971, pp. 23-26.
2. Copley, L. G., "Control of Noise by Partitions and Enclosures," Tutorial Papers on Noise Control, Inter-Noise 72, October 1972.
3. Jackson, R. S., "The Performance of Acoustic Hoods at Low Frequencies," *Acoustica,* 12, pp. 139-152, 1962.
4. Jackson, R. S., "Some Aspects of the Performance of Acoustic Hoods," *J. Sound and Vibration,* 3:1, pp. 82-94, 1966.
5. King, A. J., *The Measurement and Suppression of Noise,* Chapman & Hall, London, 1965.
6. Beranek, L. L. (ed.), *Noise and Vibration Control,* McGraw-Hill Book Co., Inc., New York, 1971.
7. Thumann, A., and Miller, R. K., *Secrets of Noise Control,* The Fairmont Press, second edition, 1976.
8. Young, R. A., "Effectiveness of Isolators in Reducing Vibration of a 250-Ton Blanking Press," *Pollution Engineering,* V 6, no. 12, December 1974, pp. 32-33.
9. Heinrich, W. H., *Industrial Accident Prevention,* McGraw-Hill, 1931.
10. Sabine, H. J., "The Absorption of Noise in Ventilating Ducts," *J. Acoustican Society of America,* Vol. 12, pp. 53-57, 1940.
11. Egan, M. D., *Concepts in Architectural Acoustics,* McGraw-Hill, 1972.
12. Doelling, N., "Noise Control for Aircraft Engine Test Cells and Ground Run-Up Suppressors," Vol. 2, *Design and Planning for Noise Control,* WADC Tech. Report 58-202(2), November, 1961, prepared under contract by Bolt, Beranek & Newman, Inc.

7

Design Guidelines
for the
"Acoustic Skin"

An "acoustic skin," also referred to as "lagging," "insulation," or "wrapping" is commonly applied to pipes that convey various types of materials. Noise as a result of fluid shock waves, turbulence, or solid impacts on the pipe can add significantly to a plant's ambient sound levels.

In unique new applications, this treatment is also being used on radiating machine components. This is particularly applicable where components have forced vibrations and vibration damping treatments would not yield effective results. This treatment can be used to contain the radiated noise similar to a machine enclosure. This chapter will present design procedures for applying the acoustical skin.

With this treatment, the radiating pipe or machine component can be enclosed with a skin-like treatment consisting of a barrier material and an absorptive layer between it and the pipe or machine component. Essentially, this treatment is an acoustical enclosure which is integral with the pipe or machine. A typical pipe lagging treatment is shown in Figure 7.1.

Important criteria in the selection of the most suitable lagging treatment for any application are:

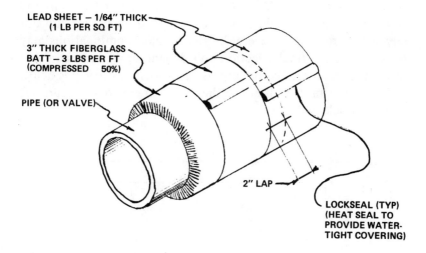

LEAD SHEET – 1/64" THICK
(1 LB PER SQ FT)

3" THICK FIBERGLASS
BATT – 3 LBS PER FT
(COMPRESSED   50%)

PIPE (OR VALVE)

2" LAP

LOCKSEAL (TYP)
(HEAT SEAL TO
PROVIDE WATER-
TIGHT COVERING)

Figure 7.1. Typical pipe lagging

1.   Noise reduction
2.   Thermal properties
3.   Ease of application
4.   Durability

DESIGN PROCEDURE

This method was developed by Johnson[1] to aid in the selection of an effective lagging configuration, based on the analysis of Schultz.[2] The primary goal of this method is proper selection for sources with significant low frequency sound pressure levels.

Accurate acoustical data of the sound source (octave band or one-third band sound pressure levels) is necessary to develop design parameters for lagging treatment. To determine the noise reduction value which the lagging treatment must achieve, the source sound levels are subtracted from the desired sound level spectrum. The lowest frequency requiring noise reduction should be identified. Using this frequency, a barrier weight and blanket thickness combination is selected from Figure 7.2. For any given frequency, several barrier/blanket combinations may be selected; the final selection will depend upon considerations of cost, space, installation, etc. If the lowest frequency is below 125 Hertz, a ratio well above the 125 Hertz curve of Figure 7.2 should be selected.

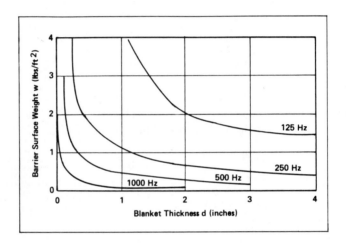

Figure 7.2
Chart for the selection of barrier surface weight and blanket thickness for insertion loss in lowest frequency octave band of interest.[1]

Once the barrier/blanket combination is selected, the noise reduction (insertion loss) may be calculated for the entire frequency spectrum. First, the frequency at which there will be zero attenuation is calculated:

$$f_o = \frac{180}{\sqrt{wd}} \qquad (7\text{-}1)$$

where: f_o = frequency of zero insertion loss, Hertz

w = barrier surface weight, pounds per square foot

d = blanket thickness, inches

This value should be plotted on octave band or one-third octave band sound pressure level graph paper.

Next, the lowest frequency is identified for which the propagation loss in the blanket provides an insertion loss of not less than 9 dB. A straight line curve will be plotted with the total insertion loss, $R_\alpha + R_\beta$, at this frequency and the zero value at f_o.

The insertion loss due to the blanket propagation attenuation, R_α, is given by:

$$R_\alpha = \beta\, d \qquad\qquad (7\text{-}2)$$

where: R_α = insertion loss due to sound propagation in blanket, dB

β = propagation loss factor of blanket, dB per inch. (This value may be obtained from manufacturer's data. Data for one material is presented in Table 7.1.)

d = blanket thickness, inches

Table 7.1
Attenuation of sound wave while traveling unit distance inside
Owens-Corning Fiberglas Type PF 105, whose average fiber diameter
is 1 micron and whose bulk density is 9.6 kg/m^3 (0.6 lb/ft^2)^2

frequency, Hz	125	250	500	1K	2K	3K	4K	6K	8K
attenuation, dB/inch	.08	.57	2.2	4.4	8.1	9.3	10.9	11.8	13.0

The insertion loss due to the transmission loss of the barrier, R_β, may be calculated from:

$$R_\beta = 10 \log \left[1 + (.037\, f\, w)^2\right] \qquad\qquad (7\text{-}3)$$

where: R_β = insertion loss due to barrier transmission loss

f = frequency, Hertz, R_α

w = barrier weight, pounds per square foot

The total insertion is calculated as the sum of $R_\alpha + R_\beta$ for the chosen frequency (where $R_\alpha > 9$ dB) and at higher frequencies. These values are then plotted and compared to the noise reduction design goals. If the required values are not achieved, the analysis procedure must be repeated with a more substantial barrier/blanket combination.

EXAMPLE

The frequency spectrum of a noise source along with the noise reduction goal is presented in Figure 7.3. The lowest frequency requiring significant reduction is 125 Hz. From Figure 7.2, a three pound per square foot barrier (w) and a 2-inch blanket (d) are chosen because there is a space limitation. The F_o value is calculated from Equation (7-1):

$$F_o = \frac{180}{\sqrt{wd}}$$

$$F_o = \frac{180}{\sqrt{3\,(2)}}$$

$$F_o = 73 \text{ Hz}$$

This value is in the 63 Hertz octave band.

The insertion loss at 2000 Hz, the lowest frequency where $R_\alpha \geq 9$ dB, is calculated from Equation (7-2):

$$R_\alpha = \beta\, d$$
$$= 8.1\,(2)$$
$$= 16.1 \text{ dB}$$

From Equation (7-3):

$$R_\beta = 10 \log \left[1 + \left(.037\,(f\,(w))\right)^2\right]$$
$$= 10 \log \left[1 + \left(.037\,(2000\,(3))\right)^2\right]$$
$$= 46 \text{ dB}$$

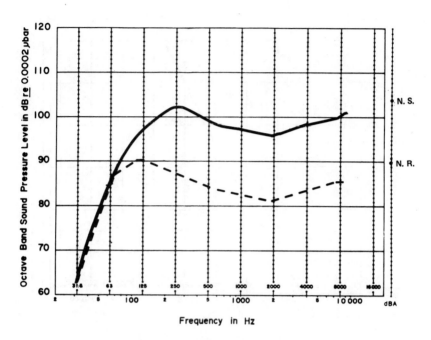

Figure 7.3
Octave band sound pressure levels of noise source (——)
and design goal (– – –) for example problem

The total insertion loss at 2000 Hertz is calculated as:

$$R = R_\alpha + R_\beta$$
$$= 16.1 + 46$$
$$\doteq 62.1 \text{ dB}$$

F_0 and the sum of R_α plus R_β are plotted at their respective frequencies and are presented in Figure 7.4.

The theoretical insertion loss exceeds the noise reduction requirements, indicating an acceptable design.

BEWARE OF TEST DATA

As shown in the design procedure of the previous section, coupling between the radiating surface and floating barrier of the lag-

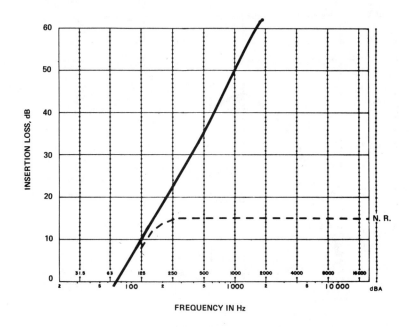

FREQUENCY IN Hz

Figure 7.4
Plot of insertion loss (—) and noise reduction
design goal (- - -) for example problem

ging treatment negates low frequency noise reduction. This coupling phenomenon will not occur when similar materials are constructed into walls or partitions. Thus, erroneous (overly optimistic) conclusions will be drawn if data developed by the procedure outlined in ASTM Standard E90-70[4] (dealing with the transmission loss of building partitions) or mass law calculations are used to predict noise reductions for lagging noise sources with significant low frequency content.

EXPERIMENTAL DATA

Noise reduction tests were conducted by Dear,[5] using standard metal B—B's in a metal pipe as the noise source, for nineteen pipe coverings. The superior coverings, selected on a cost/benefit basis, for low, medium, and high noise reduction quality are presented in Table 7.2, listed as samples A, B, and C respectively. The study by Dear made the following observations:[5]

1. Lead impregnated vinyl distinguishes itself as a covering and the function of fiber glass is to space the covering at an optimum distance from the pipe surface in a double-wall configuration and further to suppress double-wall resonance by its absorption characteristics.

2. Three- and five-inch thick amosite asbestos samples exhibited poorer performance than the one- and two-inch thicknesses on an overall basis.

3. A two-inch fiber glass spacer was consistently superior to a three-inch fiber glass spacer in all cases of comparison based upon the four-inch pipe, on a cost/benefit basis.

4. None of the pipe coverings tested exhibited good noise reduction below 500 Hz which is indicative of the real problem in controlling pipe radiation noise at these low frequencies.

5. Proper sealing of all joints in the pipe covering envelope is a critical part of achieving the available noise reduction inherent in the covering configuration.

6. Only a constrained layer laminated pipe represented a true case of structural damping. The "damping" often attributed to low modulus, wrapped insulation is a misnomer in that very little energy is removed from the pipe wall structure.

Noise reduction test values for two commercially available lagging treatments are presented as items D and E in Table 7.2. These tests were conducted with a pipe excited by a loudspeaker.

Table 7.2
Noise reduction for five pipe coverings,
dB re .0002 microbar

1/3 Octave Band Center Frequency in Hertz (Hz)	MATERIALS				
	A	B	C	D	E
200	1.8 dB	2.5 dB	2.0 dB	2.0 dB	0.0 dB
250	2.5	3.0	2.5	4.0	2.0
315	0.5	1.5	1.0	5.0	6.0
400	(−1)	1.0	1.0	5.0	6.0
500	1.5	5.0	4.5	8.0	4.5
630	0	3.0	3.5	13.0	7.0
800	1.5	4.0	4.9	16.5	9.5
1,000	4.8	12.0	13.5	16.5	11.5
1,250	6.5	17.0	17.5	22.0	16.0
1,600	9.5	18.0	19.0	22.0	16.5
2,000	13.8	24.0	26.0	24.0	17.0
2,500	14.5	23.5	28.0	24.0	18.0
3,150	30.5	26.0	28.0	29.0	20.5
4,000	22.0	28.0	31.0	31.0	27.0
5,000	26.5	33.0	35.0	30.0	30.0
6,300	30.0	35.0	37.5	28.0	29.0
8,000	31.0	36.0	38.5	29.0	29.0
10,000	33.0	35.0	39.0	–	–

A – 1-inch thick molded fiber glass (4 lbs/cu ft) with standard flame retardant aluminum foil covering. (Reference 5)

B – 1-inch thick molded fiber glass (4 lbs/cu ft) covered with a single layer of lead impregnated vinyl (0.87 lbs/sq ft). (Reference 5)

C – Same as B with 2-inch fiber glass. (Reference 5)

D – 1-inch thick polyurethane foam (2 lbs/cu ft) with lead loaded vinyl jacket (1.0 lb/sq ft). (Reference 6)

E – 2-inch thick polyurethane foam (2 lbs/cu ft) with 22 mil plastic jacket (.2 lb/sq ft). (Reference 6)

APPLICABILITY

Acoustical lagging treatments may be found to be the optimum technique for machine noise control in the following situations:

1. Where vibrations are required for material flow, such as the use of vibrators on hoppers.

2. Where vibration damping treatment would not be applicable because:

    a. vibrations are of a forced nature rather than resonant;

    b. surfaces are too irregular to apply damping treatment;

    c. the structure is too thick to dampen effectively.

3. Minimum surface area of acoustical treatment is desired as a cost saving measure.

4. Thermal insulation is also required.

5. Localized accessibility precludes the use of a total enclosure.

6. Space limitations restrict the use of a larger enclosure.

7. An acoustical treatment integral with the machine is desired for aesthetics.

TYPICAL APPLICATIONS

An acoustical lagging for piping downstream of a high pressure control valve is shown in Figure 7.5. Although new quiet valves are commercially available and may be used for new installations, this method of treatment is most common for existing installations.

Figure 7.6 demonstrates a lagging treatment for a hopper containing flour in a bakery. The vibrations could not be reduced without impeding material flow, so lagging was selected as the design solution. To meet the bakery's sanitation require-

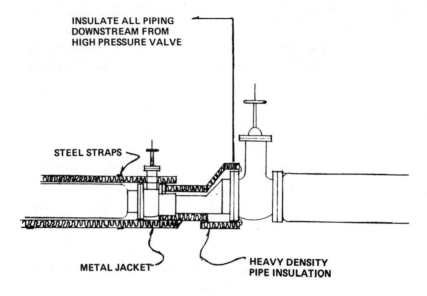

INSULATE ALL PIPING
DOWNSTREAM FROM
HIGH PRESSURE VALVE

STEEL STRAPS

METAL JACKET

HEAVY DENSITY
PIPE INSULATION

Figure 7.5. Acoustical lagging of valve piping

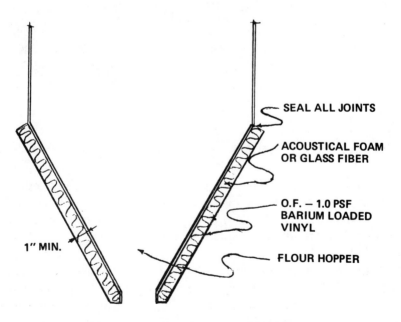

SEAL ALL JOINTS

ACOUSTICAL FOAM
OR GLASS FIBER

O.F. — 1.0 PSF
BARIUM LOADED
VINYL

FLOUR HOPPER

1″ MIN.

Figure 7.6. Acoustical lagging of flour hopper

ments, a barium loaded vinyl barrier was selected and emphasis was placed on insuring a tight seal at all joints.

Sound levels of a Jordan refiner in a pulp and paper mill may be reduced by a lagging treatment, as shown in Figure 7.7. The lagging treatment was selected rather than vibration damping because of the difficulty in damping the one-inch thick curved housing. An enclosure was not considered feasible because of accessibility requirements for maintenance and inspection. Heat build-up problems would not be expected because the equipment temperature is controlled by the temperature of the fluid flow.

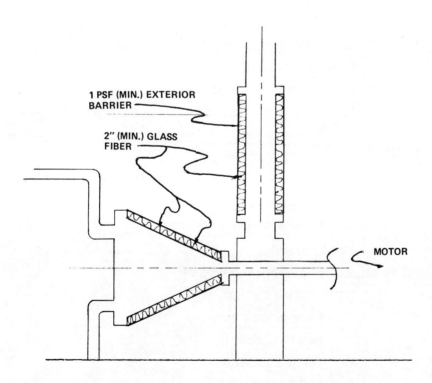

Figure 7.7. Lagging treatment for Jordan refiner

One manufacturer of a lagging treatment suggests the following potential applications:[7]

1. Power Houses, Steel Mills
    a. Casings of blowers, generators, compressors;
    b. Inlet and exhaust pipes;
    c. Steam pipes;
    d. Fan casings;
    e. Pump casings or enclosures.
2. Petro-Chemical Refineries
    a. Pipes;
    b. Blowers, generators, compressors;
    c. Gearbox enclosures;
    d. Pump casings or enclosures.
3. Heavy Fabrication
    a. Gearbox enclosures;
    b. Crane drive enclosures;
    c. Partial enclosures for presses, saws;
    d. Compressor casings;
    e. Hydraulic pump enclosures;
    f. Fan casings;
    g. Cyclone air extractor casings.
4. Food Industries
    a. Conveyor chutes, pipes;
    b. Cyclone casings;
    c. Compressor casings;
    d. Gearbox casings;
    e. Pump enclosures;
    f. Mill casings.

5. Architectural

    a. H.V.A.C. ducting;

    b. Pumps, blowers, fan casings.

6. General Manufacturing

    a. Small enclosures for gearbox;

    b. Enclosures for hydraulic pumps;

    c. Steam pipes;

    d. H.V.A.C. ducting;

    e. Compressor houses, generators;

    f. Equipment test rigs;

    g. Exhuast pipe and muffler casings;

    h. Casings of vibratory screws.

7. Plastics Industries

    a. Pelletisers;

    b. Grinders;

    c. Conveyor pipes.

REFERENCES

1. Johnson, G. E., "Design Curves to Aid in the Selection of an Effective Lagging Configuration," *Proceedings of Noisexpo,* 30 April–2 May 1975.
2. Schultz, T. J., "Wrapping, Enclosures, and Duct Linings," *Noise and Vibration Control,* L. L. Beranek ed., McGraw-Hill, New York, 1971.
3. Bies, D. A., "Acoustical Properties of Porous Materials," *Noise and Vibration Control,* L. L. Beranek ed., McGraw-Hill, New York, 1971.
4. ASTM E90–70, "Recommended Practice for Laboratory Measurement of Airborne Sound Transmission Loss of Building Partitions," Am. Soc. for Testing and Materials, Philadelphia, Pennsylvania.

5. Dear, T. A., "Noise Reduction Properties of Selected Pipe Covering Configurations," *Proceedings of Noise Con 72,* October 1972.
6. "Pipe Lagging Measured for Noise Reduction," Riverbank Acoustical Laboratories Test NR72-32 and -35, for Accessible Products Company, Tempe, Arizona 85281, 14 August 1972.
7. "Muffl-Lag," Childers Products Company, Beachwood, Ohio 44122.

8

Enclosure
Ventilation

The environment inside an acoustical enclosure is as important to an operation as the enclosure is to the employee's noise exposure.

The strain of heat build-up within a machine enclosure can affect both the product quality and the wear characteristics of its components. Heat build-up within an employee enclosure may cause extreme discomfort.

Ventilating and cooling considerations are required for most total enclosures, both on machines or employees. These requirements become critical when air-moving equipment is enclosed. This chapter illustrates design considerations for reducing heat build-up in enclosures and the silencing of enclosure venting.

HEAT GAIN

It is generally assumed that all the energy used in powering mechanical systems is eventually converted to heat. The amount of heat gained from all of the equipment must be calculated to determine:

1. cooling or ventilating necessity;
2. the effect on the equipment and process;
3. how much heat must be removed.

In most mechanical systems the heat converted is sensible heat, while in situations involving vaporization, infiltration, and fusion, there will be latent heat to be considered. Infiltration results when equipment enclosures are vented directly outdoors. In employee enclosure situations, both sensible and latent heat will be found.

All sources within the enclosure must be considered when calculating the heat gain of the operation. The main sources are:

1. Motors
2. Pumps and Machinery
3. Piping
4. Heating Equipment
5. Lights
6. People

MOTORS

The following equation is used to determine the heat gain for electric motors:

$$Q = N(H.P.)(U)(\beta) \qquad (8\text{-}1)$$

where: Q = Heat gain, BTUH

N = Number of motors

$H.P.$ = Horsepower of motor

U = % used if not continuous operation

β = Heat gain constant, BTUH/H.P. for continuous operation

The heat gain constant as a function of H.P. rating is obtained from Table 8.1.

EXAMPLE 1

Calculate the heat gain for two 15 H.P. electric motors running six hours out of an eight-hour work shift.

Table 8.1
Heat Gain from Electric Motors [1]

Nameplate Rating, HP	Approximate Efficiency	Heat Gain, BTUH per HP for Continuous Running†
Up to ¼*	60	4200
½ to 1	70	3600
1½ to 5	80	3200
7½ to 20	85	3000
Over 20	88	2900

* Including ¼ hp
† Two things are assumed when the last column is used:
(1) the motor and its load are in either the room or the air stream;
(2) the load is equal (or almost equal) to the nameplate rating.
   In general, these assumptions are true—especially for motors of 20 hp or less.

SOLUTION

$$N = 2$$
$$H.P. = 15$$
$$U = 75\%$$
$$\beta = 3000$$

$$Q = 2(15) \ .75(3000)$$
$$Q = 67,500 \text{ BTUH}$$

PUMPS

This equation is used to determine the heat gain of pumps or similar mechanical machinery:

$$Q = U_o \, A \, \Delta T \qquad (8\text{-}2)$$

where: Q =   Heat gain, BTUH

U_o =   Heat transfer coefficient of casing plus air film

$$A \quad = \quad \text{Surface area of pump, ft}^2$$

$$\Delta T \quad = \quad \text{Difference between temperature of substance pumped and ambient air, °F.}$$

The heat transfer coefficient of metal and its air film is estimated to be 0.5.

EXAMPLE 2

Find the heat gain of a pump with a surface area of 45 ft² that is pumping a hot liquid at 180°F. The ambient temperature is 78°F.

SOLUTION

$$U_o = 5°$$
$$A = 45 \text{ ft}^2$$
$$\Delta T = 180° - 78° = 102°$$
$$Q = .5 \, (45) \, 102°$$
$$Q = 2295 \text{ BTUH}$$

PIPING

The equation for approximating the heat gain due to piping of high temperature fluids in an enclosure is:

$$Q = N \, (\beta) \qquad\qquad (8\text{-}3)$$

where: $Q \quad = \quad$ Heat gain, BTUH

$N \quad = \quad$ Number of lineal feet

$\beta \quad = \quad$ Heat loss constant BTUH/ft

The heat loss constant is obtained from Table 8.2, varying with pipe diameter and insulation.

EXAMPLE 3

Find the heat gain for 10 feet of untreated 2-inch diameter pipe conveying a liquid at 180°.

Table 8.2
Heat loss from pipes [1]
(Btuh per lineal foot)

		HOT WATER, 180 F*			STEAM, PSIG*	
Pipe Size, in.	Bare	Corrugated & Laminated Asbestos, 4 Ply, 1 in. (K=0.60)	Glass Fiber, 1 in. (K=0.27)	Bare	Corrugated & Laminated Asbestos, 4 Ply, 1 in. (K=0.60)	Glass Fiber, 1 in. (K=0.27)
½	56	20	9	93	33	15
¾	68	25	12	113	38	18
1	84	29	13	139	43	20
1¼	104	33	15	172	51	23
1½	117	37	17	195	55	25
2	144	42	19	239	66	30
2½	172	49	22	285	75	34
3	206	57	26	342	8C	39
4	260	69	32	431	108	49

* Room Air Temperature, 78 F

SOLUTION

$$N = 10$$
$$\beta = 144$$
$$Q = 10 (144)$$
$$Q = 1440 \text{ BTUH}$$

HEATING EQUIPMENT

The heat gain must be calculated for heating/warming apparatus which may be either electric or gas. These heat gain values may be obtained from the manufacturer directly or estimated. For electric equipment the wattage rating on the nameplate is used with the following equation:

$$Q = N \text{ (Watts) } 3.4 \qquad (8\text{-}4)$$

where: Q = Heat gain, BTUH

N = Number of units

Watts = Rated wattage

3.4 = Heat equivalent of electric energy, BTUH/watt

For gas-burning equipment the following information should be obtained:

1. Natural gas releases 1,000 BTU/cu. ft.

2. LP gas releases 2,000 BTU/cu. ft.

3. A 2-inch natural gas burner uses 10 cu. ft./hr, 4-inch burners use 15 cu. ft./hr.

The following relationship is then used to compute an approximate heat gain:

$$Q = N \, (U) \, (\beta) \qquad\qquad (8\text{-}5)$$

where: Q = Heat gain, BTUH

N = Number of burners

U = Usage, cu. ft./hr.

β = Gas constant, BTU/cu. ft.

EXAMPLE 4

Calculate the heat gain for four 2-inch natural gas burners which heat process water.

SOLUTION

$$N = 4$$
$$U = 10$$
$$\beta = 1000$$

$$Q = 4 \, (10) \, 1000$$
$$Q = 40,000 \text{ BTUH}$$

LIGHTING

(a) Incandescent—From Equation (8-6) the heat gain from incandescent lighting fixtures can be estimated.

$$Q = \text{Watts} \times 3.4 \text{ (U)} \qquad (8\text{-}6)$$

where: Q   = Heat gain, BTUH

     Watts   = Total wattage of all incandescent fixtures

     3.4   = Heat equivalent of electric energy, BTUH/watt

     U   = % used

EXAMPLE 5

Estimate the heat gain from the lighting fixtures in a room where two 250-watt spotlights are used.

SOLUTION

$$\text{Watts} = 2\,(250) = 500$$

$$Q = 500 \times 3.4$$

$$Q = 1700 \text{ BTUH, incandescent}$$

(b) Fluorescent—To estimate the heat gain from fluorescent lighting Equation (8-7) is used:

$$Q = \text{Watts } (3.4)\,(1.2)\,(U) \qquad (8\text{-}7)$$

where: Q   = Heat gain, BTUH

     Watts   = Total wattage of all fluorescent fixtures

     3.4   = Heat equivalent of electric energy, BTUH/watt

     1.2   = Allowance factor

     U   = % used

The allowance factor is the heat gained from the ballast in the fluorescent fixture; this amounts to approximately 20 percent of the lamp's heat.

EXAMPLE 6

Calculate the heat gain from two rows of three sets of double tube 3-foot fluorescent fixtures rated at 10 watts.

SOLUTION

$$2 \times 3 \times 3' = 12$$
$$12 \times 10 \quad = 120 \text{ total wattage}$$
$$Q = 120 \,(3.4)\, 1.2$$
$$Q = 489.6 \text{ BTUH fluorescent}$$

The total heat gain for a conventional lighting system is simulated by examples 5 and 6. For continuous operation, the total heat gain would be 2189.6 BTUH.

PEOPLE (Body Heat)

The heat released from the human body varies with the individual and the degree of his activity. Both the sensible and latent heat that is released must be used in the calculation. Table 8.3 presents the heat gains, sensible and latent, for an average human body engaged in several physical activities.

This equation is used to calculate the heat gain from people in employee enclosures:

$$Q = N_i U_i \,(S_i + L_i) \qquad\qquad (8\text{-}8)$$

where: Q = Heat gain, BTUH

N = Number of people

S_i = Sensible heat gain from a physical activity, BTUH

L_i = Latent heat gain from a physical activity, BTUH

U = % inside enclosure

EXAMPLE 7

Calculate the heat gain in an employee enclosure if two employees are assigned desk work and three employees are inspectors spending 75 percent of their time outside the enclosure.

Table 8.3

Heat gain from occupants of conditioned spaces[1]

Degree of activity	Typical Application	Total Heat Adults, Male BTU/HR	Total Heat Adjusted[2] BTU/HR	Sensible Heat BTU/HR	Latent Heat BTU/HR
Seated at rest	Theater-matinee	390	330	200	130
	Theater-evening	390	350	215	135
Seated, very light work	Offices, Hotels, Apartments	450	400	215	185
Moderately active office work	Offices, Hotels, Apartments	475	450	220	230
Standing, light work; or Walking slowly	Retail and Department stores	550	450	220	230
Walking; Seated Standing; Walking slowly	Drug store Bank	550	400	220	280
Sedentary work	Restaurant[3]	490	550	240	310
Light bench work	Factory	800	750	240	510
Moderate dancing	Dance Hall	900	850	270	580
Walking 3 mph; Moderately heavy work	Factory	1000	1000	330	670
Bowling[4]	Bowling Alley	1500	1450	510	940
Heavy work	Factory	1500	1450	510	940

Reprinted by permission from 1965 ASHRAE GUIDE and Data Book.
NOTES:
1 Tabulated values are based on 78 F for dry-bulb temperature.
2 Adjusted total heat gain is based on normal percentage of men, women, and children for the application listed, with the postulate that the gain from an adult female is 85 per cent of that for an adult male, and the gain from a child is 75 per cent of that for an adult male.
3 Adjusted total heat value for sedentary work, restaurant, includes 60 Btuh for food per individual (30 Btu sensible and 30 Btu latent).
4 For bowling figure one person per alley actually bowling, and all others as sitting (400 Btuh) or standing (550 Btuh).

SOLUTION

$$N_1 = 2$$
$$N_2 = 3$$
$$S_1 = 220$$
$$S_2 = 270$$
$$L_1 = 230$$
$$L_2 = 580$$
$$U_2 = .25$$

$$Q = 2\ (220 + 230) + 3\ (.25)\ (270 + 580)$$
$$Q = 1537.5\ \text{BTUH}$$

To find the total heat gain in a machine or employee enclosure, simply add the heat gains calculated for each piece of equipment.

EXAMPLE 8

Calculate the total heat gain, Q_T, in a machine enclosure using situations presented previously for one motor, one pump, one water heater plus piping, and two spotlights.

SOLUTION

Heat Gain from Example 1; motor
$$67,500 \div 2 = 33,750\ \text{BTUH}$$

Heat Gain from Example 2; pump
$$2295\ \text{BTUH}$$

Heat Gain from Example 3; pipe
$$1440\ \text{BTUH}$$

Heat Gain from Example 4; water heating
$$40,000\ \text{BTUH}$$

Heat Gain from Example *5(a)*; lights
1700 BTUH

$$Q_T = 67,500 + 2295 + 1440 + 40,000 + 1700$$
$$= 112,935 \text{ BTUH}$$

EXAMPLE 9

Calculate the total heat gain, Q_T, in an employee enclosure for situations similar to the examples of fluorescent lighting and human body.

SOLUTION

Heat Gain from Example 6; lights
489.6 BTUH

Heat Gain from Example 7; employee
1537.5 BTUH

$$Q_T = 489.6 + 1537.5 = 2027.1 \text{ BTUH}$$

VENTILATING

Having calculated the total heat gained from the equipment or people within an enclosure, the air required to control the temperature of the interior environment can be determined. For small enclosures, especially the employee type, one change of the room's air volume per minute prevents heat build-up exceeding 15° and provides an adequate amount of fresh air. This holds true only if:

$$V \geq .06 \, Q \qquad (8\text{-}9)$$

where: V = Enclosure volume, ft³

Q = Heat gained, BTUH

If this does not hold true, the volume of air, CFM, must be calculated by using the equation:

$$CFM = \frac{Q}{1.08 \, (\Delta T)} \qquad (8\text{-}10)$$

where: CFM = Cubic feet per minute

Q = Heat gain, BTUH

ΔT = Temperature difference between environments (inside temperature—ambient temperature), °F.

EXAMPLE 10

From Example 8, the heat gain within an enclosure due to a hot water pumping system is 112,935 BTUH. If the enclosure is 12' X 12' X 6', what CFM is required to maintain a temperature increase no greater than 15°F?

SOLUTION

$$CFM = \frac{112.935}{1.08 \, (15)}$$

$$CFM = 6971.3$$

The additional heat gained by the fan's motor must also be removed (when it is located in the enclosure or supply duct). The CFM required should be increased by approximately 10 percent to accommodate the additional heat. This increases the air required to 7668.4 CFM.

This increase can be avoided by placing the motor outside the unit (the enclosure and ductwork) or locating it at the exit of the duct and have it exhaust the air.

SILENCING

The exhaust and the intake openings must be silenced so as not to defeat the original purpose of the enclosure. There are many commercially available silencers for this purpose as presented in Chapter 11. Also, fabricated duct configurations, as illustrated in Figures 8.1, 8.2, and 8.3 can provide adequate results at sub-

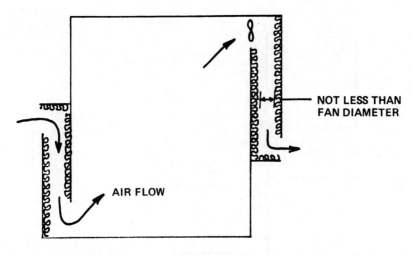

NOT LESS THAN
FAN DIAMETER

AIR FLOW

Figure 8.1
Duct system for ventilation of acoustical enclosure

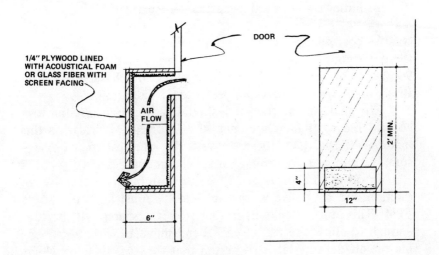

1/4" PLYWOOD LINED
WITH ACOUSTICAL FOAM
OR GLASS FIBER WITH
SCREEN FACING

DOOR

AIR
FLOW

2' MIN.

4"

12"

6"

Figure 8.2
Sound trap for supply air port in enclosure

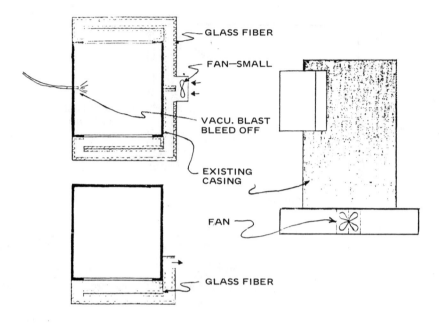

Figure 8.3
Acoustical enclosure and sound traps for roots blower system

stantial cost savings. The sound attenuation required would be the determining factor in selecting the length and type (straight, 90° bend, or 180° bend). The noise reduction characteristics of these three types of ducts are presented in Chapter 6.

The material of the duct should have a transmission loss comparable to that of the enclosures. For easy fabrication the material of the duct doesn't have to be identical to the enclosure, but should have similar barrier characteristics.

In order to achieve good results, both in terms of noise reduction and air delivery, the air velocity must be kept ≤ 500 FPM. This insures that operating static pressures will be low enough to allow the use of 180°-bend-silencers without impeding the air delivery. It is suggested that for large systems which have high CFM requirements and use fans with static pressures greater than 1.0″ w.g., commercially available silencers should be employed.

DUCT SIZING

This section is used to determine the dimensions for enclosure silencers. More in-depth calculations must be performed for the connecting ductwork when an existing HVAC system is to be used. Duct sizing is best accomplished with a friction loss chart, as shown in Figure 8.4. The Trane Company also provides a calculator which may be used for this purpose.

The intersection of the air volume, CFM (previously calculated) with the desired velocity, FPM, in Figure 8.4 will indicate the friction loss or static pressure per 100 feet and the required duct size (round or rectangular). For best results, the velocity should not exceed 500 FPM. The size determined is the interior dimension required to convey the air properly, and sound absorption and wall material thicknesses are in addition to those dimensions.

EXAMPLE 11

The sound level in an enclosure is 100 dBA and the dominant frequency is 500 Hertz. The air required to properly ventilate the enclosure is 900 CFM. Determine the construction of a silencer for the enclosure.

SOLUTION

Using Figure 8.4 with a maximum velocity of 500 FPM, the static pressure of the duct is equal to .02" w.g. The duct silencer dimensions would be approximately 18" in diameter or 1' X 2'. From Figure 2.6, a 2" thick sound absorption material, such as glass fiber should be used. The duct should be constructed of ¼-inch plywood which provides 20 dB of transmission loss at 500 C.P.S. This would make the actual duct dimensions 22.5" in diameter or 1'4.5". The length would be 4' as calculated from Figure 6.4, and provides attenuation of 28 dB.

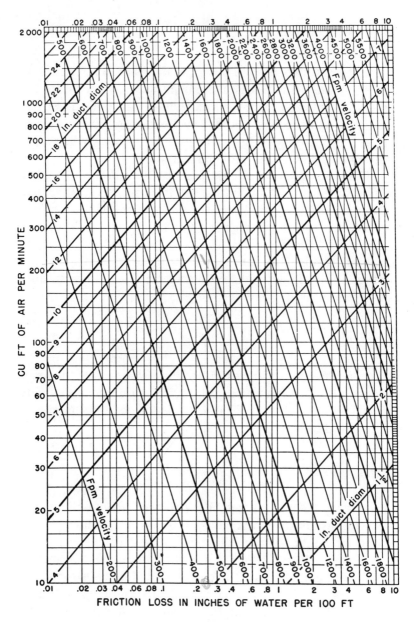

(Based on Standard Air of 0.075 lb per cu ft density flowing through average, clean, round, galvanized metal ducts having approximately 40 joints per 100 ft)

Figure 8.4. Friction chart for air[1]

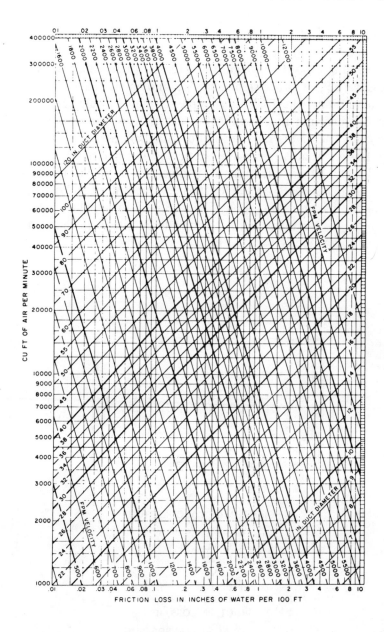

Figure 8.4 (continued)

FAN SELECTION

In selecting a fan to provide the CFM required, the total static pressure, SP, of the system must be known. Through the previous equations, the CFM requirements may be calculated. Figure 8.5 presents the step-by-step calculations for an enclosure silencer. The Industrial Ventilation Manual[2] and the Engineering Design Manual[3] provide static losses for elbows, fittings, bends, etc. Steps 1 through 6 involve data from the two manuals. Step 7 is based on the length previously sized and obtained from the friction loss graph, Figure 8.4. Additional CFM losses from 90° mitre turns were not considered due to the extremely low supply velocity, ≤500 FPM.

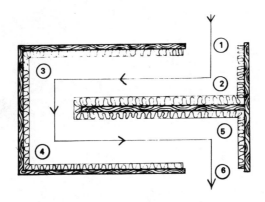

SUMMARY OF CALCULATION

1 = .01   ENTRY LOSS
2 = .02   90° BEND
3 = .02   90° BEND
4 = .02   90° BEND
5 = .02   90° BEND
6 = .01   EXIT LOSS
7 = .002 FRICTION LOSS, 10′

.102 TOTAL STATIC PRESSURE

Figure 8.5
Calculation of total static pressure for 180° bend duct silencer

When arriving at the total static pressure for an entire system that has a plenum effect, the velocity pressure, VP, is an additional factor. When air enters and exits an enclosure or plenum from a duct, the entire velocity pressure is converted to static pressure. Table 8.4 from the Engineering Design Manual by United Sheet Metal Corporation relates velocities, V, FPM, to velocity pressures, VP. Figure 8.6 presents an entire enclosure system and the calculated total static pressure the fan would have to work against. The SP for the 180° bend muffler independent of the friction loss due to length may be used as a constant figure that is adaptable to all slow velocity systems (≤ 500 FPM).

Table 8.4
Velocity pressure VP, inches W.G.–Velocity V, fpm

VP	V	VP	V	VP	V	VP	V
.01	400	.25	2003	.49	2804	.73	3422
.02	566	.26	2042	.50	2832	.74	3445
.03	694	.27	2081	.51	2860	.75	3468
.04	801	.28	2119	.52	2888	.76	3491
.05	896	.29	2157	.53	2916	.77	3514
.06	981	.30	2194	.54	2943	.78	3537
.07	1060	.31	2230	.55	2970	.79	3560
.08	1133	.32	2266	.56	2997	.80	3582
.09	1202	.33	2301	.57	3024	.81	3605
.10	1266	.34	2335	.58	3050	.82	3627
.11	1328	.35	2369	.59	3076	.83	3649
.12	1387	.36	2403	.60	3102	.84	3671
.13	1444	.37	2436	.61	3128	.85	3692
.14	1499	.38	2469	.62	3154	.86	3714
.15	1551	.39	2501	.63	3179	.87	3736
.16	1602	.40	2533	.64	3204	.88	3757
.17	1651	.41	2564	.65	3229	.89	3778
.18	1699	.42	2596	.66	3254	.90	3799
.19	1746	.43	2626	.67	3278	.91	3821
.20	1791	.44	2657	.68	3303	.92	3841
.21	1835	.45	2687	.69	3327	.93	3862
.22	1879	.46	2716	.70	3351	.94	3883
.23	1920	.47	2746	.71	3375	.95	3904
.24	1962	.48	2775	.72	3398	.96	3924

/more/

Table 8.4 (continued)

VP	V	VP	V	VP	V	VP	V
.97	3944	1.46	4839	1.98	5636	3.00	6937
.98	3965	1.48	4872	2.00	5664	3.04	6983
.99	3985	1.50	4905	2.04	5720	3.08	7028
1.00	4005	1.52	4938	2.08	5776	3.12	7074
1.02	4045	1.54	4970	2.12	5831	3.16	7119
1.04	4084	1.56	5002	2.16	5886	3.20	7164
1.06	4123	1.58	5034	2.20	5940	3.24	7209
1.08	4162	1.60	5066	2.24	5994	3.28	7253
1.10	4200	1.62	5098	2.28	6047	3.32	7297
1.12	4238	1.64	5129	2.32	6100	3.36	7341
1.14	4276	1.66	5160	2.36	6153	3.40	7385
1.16	4313	1.68	5191	2.40	6205	3.44	7428
1.18	4351	1.70	5222	2.44	6256	3.48	7471
1.20	4387	1.72	5253	2.48	6307	3.52	7514
1.22	4424	1.74	5283	2.52	6358	3.56	7556
1.24	4460	1.76	5313	2.56	6408	3.60	7599
1.26	4496	1.78	5343	2.60	6458	3.64	7641
1.28	4531	1.80	5373	2.64	6507	3.68	7683
1.30	4566	1.82	5403	2.68	6556	3.72	7724
1.32	4601	1.84	5433	2.72	6605	3.76	7766
1.34	4636	1.86	5462	2.76	6654	3.80	7807
1.36	4671	1.88	5491	2.80	6702	3.84	7848
1.38	4705	1.90	5521	2.84	6749	3.88	7889
1.40	4739	1.92	5549	2.88	6797	3.92	7929
1.42	4773	1.94	5578	2.92	6844	3.96	7970
1.44	4806	1.96	5607	2.96	6891	4.00	8010

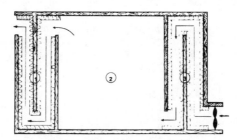

TOTAL STATIC PRESSURE CALCULATION
1 = .102 180° BEND SILENCER
2 = .020 ENCLOSURE
3 = .102 180° BEND SILENCER
.224 TOTAL STATIC PRESSURE

Figure 8.6
Calculation of total static pressure for acoustical enclosure system

COOLING OR LOWERING
HEAT BUILD-UP

The discussion and calculations presented previously have outlined the procedure for ventilating an enclosure with fresh air to achieve minimal heat build-up. Some mechanical operations will not tolerate any heat build-up, or, as in employee enclosures, a temperature reduction is necessary.

It is possible to use Equation (8-10) to provide the air volume that would allow nearly no temperature build-up (1°F minimum).

EXAMPLE 12

If the enclosure in Example 10 could not tolerate more than a 5° heat build-up, what CFM would be required?

SOLUTION

$$CFM = \frac{112,935}{1.08\ (5)}$$

$$CFM = 96,823.6$$

It can be seen when heat build-up of 1°F is approached, the CFM required equals the BTUH gained. In small enclosures or low heat gain operations, the use of ambient air for heat reduction may be acceptable. But in situations involving large heat gains, as in Example 12, or where human comfort considerations are involved, this is not economically feasible. Introducing cool or cold conditioned air to reduce the temperature can be achieved with air-conditioners.

An air-conditioner rated to cool the amount of BTUs gained by the operation should be selected. It should be remembered that when the air-conditioner is running its economy is a function of the amount of cycling of the unit. So selecting a unit with a cooling capacity equal to or slightly less than the heat gain, considering maximum ambient heat, will minimize its cycle time. The unit should have separate controls so it may be shut off whenever possible to save energy consumption.

Extreme environmental conditions which exist in many plants require that attention must be given to proper selection of air-conditioner units. Most commercially available air-conditioners intended for home use are not reliable enough to make them suitable for some applications. They are not designed to operate when temperature is quite high and there is abrasive dust in the air. Many are not made to take the abuse that industrial equipment must withstand. Unexpected failure of an air-conditioner may result in unbearable temperatures within an enclosure and in extreme cases, cause shut-down of an operation.

The following relationship may be used to calculate the required air temperature and/or air volume necessary for a given temperature change:

$$\Delta T = \frac{Q}{1.08\ V} \qquad\qquad (8\text{-}11)$$

where: ΔT = change in air supply temperature, °F

Q = change in sensible heat content, BTUH

V = volume of air, CFM

EXAMPLE 13

In a hot water pumping system with a heat gain of 112,935 BTUH, a heat gain of 15°F results when 6971 CFM of ambient air is supplied. Rather than supply 96,824 CFM of ambient air to prevent a heat build-up of greater than 5°F, cool air at a lower CFM may be used. The ambient air temperature is 72°F. Calculate the required temperature of the supply air if the same 6971 CFM is to be used.

SOLUTION

$$\Delta T = \frac{112,935}{1.08\ (6971)}$$

$$= 15.1°F$$

$$T_s = T_a + T_{bu} - \Delta T$$

$$= 72° + 5° - 15.1°$$

$$= 61.9°F$$

In an employee enclosure where both ventilating and cooling are important, a fixed air volume should be used to insure fresh air is supplied to the employees. A fixed rate of one air volume change per minute is typically used.

EXAMPLE 14

In an enclosure 18′ X 12′ X 7.5′, and a total heat gain of 34,900 BTUH, find the temperature of the supply air required to maintain a 20° reduction in a 90° environment. One air volume change per minute is necessary for ventilation.

SOLUTION

$$CFM = volume = 18' \times 12' \times 7.5'$$
$$= 1620 \text{ ft}^3$$
$$\Delta T = \frac{34{,}900}{1.08 \times 1620}$$
$$= 19.9°$$
$$T_s = T_a + T_{bu} - \Delta T$$
$$= 90° + 20° - 19.9°$$
$$= 50.1°F$$

REFERENCES

1. The Trane Company, "Trane Air Conditioning Manual," Fifty-first printing, May 1976.
2. "Industrial Ventilation," American Conference of Government Industrial Hygienists, 14th edition, 1976.
3. "Engineering Design Manual," United Steel Metal Corp., Bulletin 100-1.676.

9

Design Guidelines
for Barriers

Acoustical barriers are commonly used for the control of outdoor sound propagation. One example is traffic noise barriers
along highways. In outdoor applications where the surrounding
environment is free field, barriers are effective and predictable.

Barriers are also feasible for indoor noise control where
machine noise must be attenuated only a modest amount and
for machines that cannot be completely or permanently enclosed. When used indoors, however, barrier effectiveness is
limited by the reverberation characteristics of the interior space.

FREE FIELD BARRIER ANALYSIS

If sound waves did not bend, barriers would be the perfect noise
isolators, However, due to the diffraction characteristics, sound
waves bend over a barrier toward the observer. The parameters
which affect the degree of acoustical attenuation are the distance between both the sound source and the wall, and the wall
and the observer, the wavelength of the sound, and the sound
transmission loss of the barrier.

Since acoustical barriers have been the subject of analysis
since 1896,[1] it is not surprising that barrier analysis techniques
vary in the published literature. Important contributions to the
analysis of barriers have been made by Redferan,[2] Fehr,[3]
Rettinger,[4] Maekawa,[5] Rathe,[6] Kurze and Beranek,[7] and

Pierce.[8] A review of the literature on barriers was recently published by Kurze.[9]

The most commonly used model for barrier attenuation calculation was developed by Maekawa.[5] The model has been experimentally verified with actual free field barriers. Maekawa's analysis is based on asymptotic results of the optical-diffraction theory.

Utilizing the barrier geometry of Figure 9.1, the Fresnel number is defined as:

$$N = \frac{2}{\lambda}(x+y-z) \qquad (9\text{-}1)$$

where: N = Fresnel number (dimensionless)

$x+y$ = path length over barrier, feet

z = straight-line distance between source and receiver, feet

λ = wavelength of sound, feet

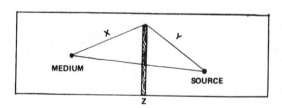

Figure 9.1. Acoustic barrier parameters

The acoustical attenuation, as a function of the Fresnel number, may be determined from Figure 9.2.

This analysis is valid only where the receiver is in the shadow zone of the barrier, or N is greater than zero. When N ranges from −0.2 to 0 (the barrier does not block the line of sight path between the source and receiver) attenuations may range between 0 and 5 dB. The practical limit for maximum barrier attenuation is 24 dB. To be effective, a barrier must be nonporous and have a transmission loss 6 dB higher than the barrier noise reduction value at every frequency.

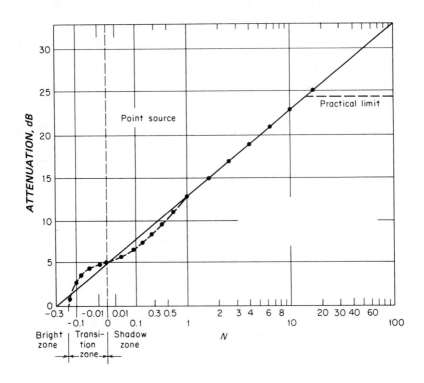

Figure 9.2
Barrier attenuation as a function of the Fresnel number[7]

The sound wavelength may be calculated from:

$$\lambda = \frac{c}{f} \qquad (9\text{-}2)$$

where: c = speed of sound, ft/sec
         f = frequency, Hertz

At 70°F (21.1°C), the speed of sound is 1,128 ft/sec, resulting in a wavelength of approximately one foot. At other
temperatures, the speed of sound may be calculated from:

$$c = 49.03\sqrt{R} \qquad (9\text{-}3)$$

where: R = absolute temperature, degrees Rankine

note: °R = °F + 459.7

         °R = °K (1.8)

         °K = °C + 273.2

         °F = $\frac{9}{5}$ °C + 273

Where actual barrier calculations are not performed, a "rule of thumb" is that the barrier must create a shadow zone of approximately 30°, as shown in Figure 9.3, to be effective.

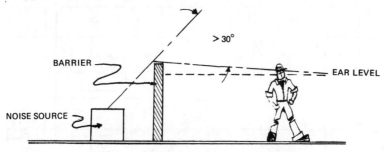

Figure 9.3
Acoustical barrier showing 30° angle
required for acoustical effectiveness.

INDOOR BARRIERS ANALYSIS

Free field conditions exist in outdoor spaces, and sound levels will attenuate at a rate of 6 decibels with each doubling of distance from the source. Sound reflections from wall and ceiling surfaces create a reverberant sound field in indoor spaces. In areas where the reflected sound is greater than the direct sound, a diffuse sound field exists, with sound approaching a receiver from all directions. Since acoustical barriers are constructed to block the direct source-to-receiver sound path, they are ineffective where diffuse sound fields exist. The transition from a directional sound field to a diffuse sound field in a room occurs at a distance from the noise source given by:

$$r = 0.14\sqrt{\alpha S} \qquad (9\text{-}4)$$

where: r   = distance from source, ft.

$\bar{\alpha}$ = average sound absorption coefficient

S   = total surface area of the interior space, ft^2

The regions of the direct and reverberant sound fields may also be identified as a function of the room constant, as shown in Figure 9.4.

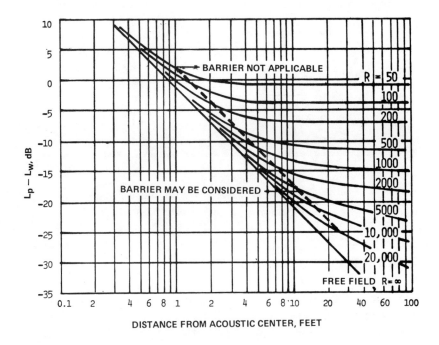

Figure 9.4
Regions of free field and reverberant field
sound levels as a function of the room constant

As an initial analysis, it should be recognized that if a receiver is located in the reverberant sound field, the placement of a barrier between the source and receiver will probably not provide significant attenuation.

A more detailed analysis of indoor barrier performance was developed by Moreland and Musa.[10] In analyzing a barrier as a partition between a source room and a receiver room, the insertion loss is:

$$\text{I.L.} = 10 \log_{10} \left[\frac{\dfrac{QD}{4\pi r^2} + \dfrac{4\,K_1\,K_2}{S(1-K_1\,K_2)}}{\dfrac{Q}{4\pi r^2} + \dfrac{4}{S_o\,\alpha_o}} \right] \qquad (9\text{-}5)$$

where:

IL = insertion loss, decibels

Q = source directivity factor

r = distance between source and receiver in the absence of the barrier

$S_o\alpha_o$ = the room absorption for the original room before inserting the barrier where S_o is the total room surface area and α_o is the mean room absorption coefficient

S = the open area between the barrier perimeter and the room walls and ceiling

D = the diffraction coefficient, given by

$$= \sum \frac{1}{3 + 10\,N_i} \qquad (9\text{-}6)$$

N_i = the Fresnel number for diffraction around the ith edge of the barrier

K_1 & K_2 = dimensionless numbers related to the room absorption on the source side ($S_1\alpha_1$), and the receiver side ($S_2\alpha_2$) of the barrier, respectively, as well as the open area, S. These numbers are given by:

$$K_1 = \frac{S}{S + S_1\,\alpha_1} \qquad (9\text{-}7)$$

$$K_2 = \frac{S}{S + S_2\,\alpha_2} \qquad (9\text{-}8)$$

The insertion loss due to a barrier where the source room is reflective and the receiver room is reflective is given by:

$$\text{I.L.} = 10 \log_{10} \left[\frac{\dfrac{QD}{4\pi r^2} + \dfrac{4}{S_1 \alpha_1 + S}}{\dfrac{Q}{4\pi r^2} + \dfrac{4}{S_0 \alpha_0}} \right] \qquad (9\text{-}9)$$

The insertion loss where the receiver room is absorptive and the source room is reflective may be calculated from:

$$\text{I.L.} = 10 \log_{10} \left[\frac{\dfrac{QD}{4\pi r^2} + \dfrac{4}{S_2 \alpha_2 + S}}{\dfrac{Q}{4\pi r^2} + \dfrac{4}{S_0 \alpha_0}} \right] \qquad (9\text{-}10)$$

A computer analysis by Lowe[11] provides illustration of the acoustical performance of barriers. Figure 9.5 shows the influence of barrier size on free field (outdoor) attenuation. The influence of ordinary and acoustical ceilings on barrier attenuation are shown in Figure 9.6. Figure 9.7 demonstrates the effectiveness of a three-sided booth in various indoor environments.

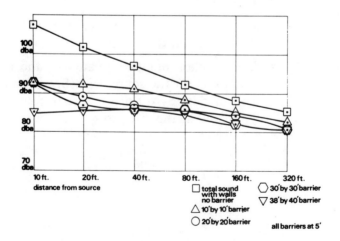

Figure 9.5. Effect of barrier size on attenuation[11]

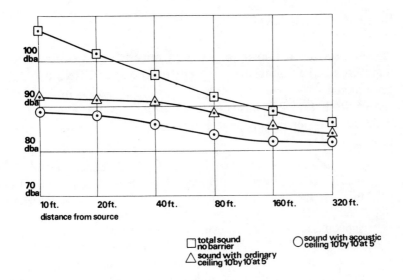

Figure 9.6. Ceiling absorption effect on barrier attenuation[11]

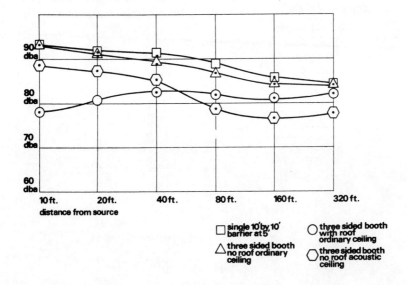

Figure 9.7. Noise reduction of partial enclosure[11]

ROLL-AWAY BARRIERS

A common noise exposure problem arises due to exposure of maintenance personnel who are within the sound field of adjacent machinery while making repairs. The following design, shown in Figure 9.8 was reported to reduce noise exposure to maintenance personnel in a compressor building from 98 dBA to 86 dBA:[12]

> One approach to providing a zone of reduced noise level is the installation of a series of 12-ft-high, 4-inch-thick acoustic panels. The modules are steel with glass fiber fill mounted on caster wheel assemblies. The design of each modular panel section is such that the support assemblies will provide a low center of gravity to prevent tipping. The casters allow easy movement so one man can roll each panel in place. When not in use the portable panels are stored in a corner or other open space within the compressor building. Lift lugs are provided atop each panel for movement by overhead crane. Wheel brakes are attached to each wheel caster for fixed positioning. On the side of each panel along each edge is a flange in which the next modular panel will nest. This assists alignment where floors are uneven. Additional adjustment is available on each caster assembly for uneven floor sections.

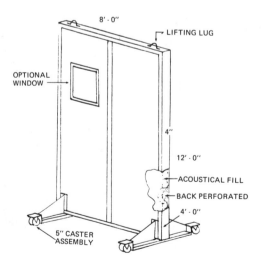

Figure 9.8. Dimensional sketch of roll-away acoustical barrier[12]

EXPERIMENTAL DESIGN

The best method to insure the effectiveness of a permanent barrier system is to first assess experimental noise reduction with a temporary barrier. A heavy cardboard barrier should be sufficient for assessment purposes where only a 5-10 dBA noise reduction is anticipated, and a plywood experimental barrier may be constructed where the barrier is to provide a greater noise reduction.

REFERENCES

1. Sommerfeld, A., *Math. Ann.* 47, 1896, pp. 317-374.
2. Redferan, S. W., "Some Acoustical Source-Observer Problems," *Phil. Mag.,* Ser. 7, Vol. 30, 1940, pp. 223-236.
3. Fehr, R. O., "The Reduction of Industrial Machine Noise," *Proceedings of the 2nd Noise Abatement Symposium,* Armour Research Foundation, Chicago, 1951, pp. 93-103.
4. Rettinger, M., "Noise Level Reduction by Barriers," *Noise Control,* Sept. 1957.
5. Maekawa, Z., "Noise Reduction by Screens," *Memoirs of the Faculty of Engineering,* Kobe University, Japan, Vol. 12, 1966, pp. 1-12.
6. Rathe, E. J., "Note on Two Common Problems of Sound Propagation," *Journal of Sound and Vibration,* Vol. 10, 1969, pp. 472-479.
7. Kurze, U., and Beranek, L. L., "Sound Propagation Outdoors," in: *Noise and Vibration Control,* Beranek, L. L. (Ed.), Chapter 7, McGraw-Hill Book Co., New York, 1971.
8. Pierce, A. D., "Noise Diffraction: Suggested Estimation Procedures," *Inter-Noise 72 Proceedings,* Washington, D.C., Oct. 4–6, 1972, pp. 110-115.

9.   Kurze, U. J., "Noise Reduction by Barriers," *Journal of the Acoustical Society of America*, 55, 1974, pp. 504-518.

10.   Moreland, J. B., and Musa, R. S., "The Performance of Acoustic Barriers," *Inter-Noise 72 Proceedings*, Washington, D.C., Oct. 4–6, 1972, pp. 95-104.

11.   Paddock, S. G., "Roll-Away Acoustic Barriers for Isolating Machinery Noise," *Pollution Engineering*.

12.   Lowe, A. W., "The Effectiveness of Barriers Under Extended Ceilings," *Inter-Noise 72 Proceedings*, Washington, D.C., Oct. 4–6, 1972, pp. 89-94.

10

Guidelines for Economic Assessment of Enclosure Systems

An economic analysis is an important aspect of any noise control program. Until 24 August 1976, the Occupational Safety and Health Administration did not formally recognize economic factors as related to the feasibility of a noise control program. On that date, the Occupational Safety and Health Review Commission ruled in a case involving the Continental Can Company that the Labor Department must consider economic as well as technical aspects of feasibility. In his lead opinion, Commission Chairman Frank R. Barnako stated that in determining whether controls are economically feasible, relevant cost and benefit factors must be weighed, but that controls may be economically feasible even though they are expensive and increase production costs.

While the commission cannot establish specific guidelines which would apply to all cases, Barnako said, assessment of the cost/benefit of noise control should take into account the number of employees exposed to excessive noise and the net reduction in their exposure that controls can reasonably be expected to produce. Costs must include the direct expense of installing and maintaining controls and indirect expenses due to loss of productivity or efficiency.[1]

COST-EFFECTIVENESS ANALYSIS

The effectiveness-cost ratio of a noise reduction measure may be computed by dividing the effectiveness factor, E, by the cost, C, of noise abatement:

$$E/C = \frac{\Sigma \Delta D_1}{C} \qquad (10\text{-}1)$$

where: ΔD_1 = reduction in noise dose of each employee due to a noise reduction measure.

The E/C ratio is a measure of hearing risk reduction per unit capital investment. Thus, for the same capital investment, the alternative solution with the highest E/C ratio would be the better project.

RATE OF RETURN

Capital investments are necessary to convert noise-reduction proposals to reality. A fundamental principle of all investments is that dollars in hand are worth more than dollars to be received in the future. Therefore, investing dollars today in a noise-reduction project permits annual savings of operating dollars over the life of the investment. Thus, a time value is placed on all cash flows into and out of the company.

The rate of return of an investment before taxes is a simple indicator of the relative economic merit of the investment. Two equations can be used to compute rate of return:

$$C = \frac{R}{P} \qquad (10\text{-}2)$$

$$C = \frac{i(1 + i)^n}{(1 + i)^n - 1} \qquad (10\text{-}3)$$

where: C = capital recovery factor

R = uniform series of payments, in dollars, occurring at end of each interest period (payments include annual operating and maintenance costs)

P = present worth of investment at beginning of interest period, dollars

i = desired rate of return (interest rate)

n = number of periods interest is compounded

Equation (10-2) represents the ratio of net operating savings to capital investment. The equation can be used to compute the capital recovery factor. The factor, in turn, is used to compute the before-tax rate of return of a noise-reduction investment. Equation (10-3) or the abbreviated interest table, Table 10.1, can be used to determine the approximate rate of return, once the capital recovery factor has been computed.

Table 10.1

	CAPITAL RECOVERY FACTORS								
Period, Yr	Capital Recovery Factor When Before-Tax Rate of Return Is (Percent):								
	8	10	12	15	20	25	30	40	50
5	0.25046	0.26380	0.27741	0.29832	0.33438	0.37185	0.41058	0.49136	0.57583
10	0.14903	0.16275	0.17698	0.19925	0.23852	0.28007	0.32346	0.41432	0.50882
15	0.11683	0.13147	0.14682	0.17102	0.21388	0.25912	0.30598	0.40259	0.50114
20	0.10185	0.11746	0.13388	0.15976	0.20536	0.25292	0.30159	0.40048	0.50015
25	0.09368	0.11017	0.12750	0.15470	0.20212	0.25095	0.30043	0.40009	–
30	0.08883	0.10608	0.12414	0.15230	0.20085	0.25031	0.30011	–	–

EXAMPLE

Two techniques are being considered to reduce employee exposure to machine noise by 15 decibels (dB). The first method involves installing a $5000 noise barrier between the source and the workers. Plant production costs are estimated to be boosted $2000 a year because of the barrier. The second technique consists of building a $4000 enclosure around the machine. Production costs are expected to increase $2500 annually because of the enclosure. Which technique has the lower owning cost? Assume a 15% desired before-tax rate of return and an expected equipment life of 20 years.

SOLUTION

Equation values are:

$$P = 5000 \text{ for barrier, } 4000 \text{ for enclosure}$$
$$n = 20 \text{ for barrier, } 20 \text{ for enclosure}$$

From the interest table:

$$C = 0.15976 \text{ for barrier}$$
$$0.15976 \text{ for enclosure}$$
$$(i = 15, n = 20)$$

Using Equation (10-2):

$$R = P \times C$$
$$R = 5000 \times 0.15976$$
$$= \$799 \text{ for barrier}$$
$$R = 4000 \times 0.15976$$
$$= \$639 \text{ for enclosure}$$

Total annual owning cost is equal to the increase in production cost plus the operating and maintenance costs. For the noise barrier:

$$2000 + 799 = \$2799$$

For the enclosure:

$$2500 + 639 = \$3139$$

Thus, the annual owning cost of the noise barrier is $340 lower than for the enclosure. The noise barrier is the more economical alternative.

ENCLOSURE COSTS

A 1973 report published by the U.S. Department of Labor[3] indicated that the cost of machine enclosures may range from $1500 for simple total enclosures, such as for screw machines, to $40,000 for complex enclosures, such as for special presses. The cost of personnel enclosures was estimated to range from

$3000 to $15,000, with an average cost of $8,000. Partitions were estimated to typically cost $8 per square foot.

A compilation of typical costs for materials which may be utilized in the construction of acoustical enclosures and barriers is presented in Table 10.2.[2]

The estimated costs for enclosures of various constructions are presented in Table 10.3.[4] The enclosure design used in the estimates is 4 ft. wide X 9 ft. long X 8 ft. high and designed for an automatic punch press.

Table 10.2
Acoustical Material Cost Summary[2]

Material	Cost ($/sq ft)
4" Acoustical Panel	5.00–10.00
2" Acoustical Panel	3.00–6.00
Lead Sheet, 1 psf	.40–.75
Lead-Vinyl Sheet, 1 psf	1.70–3.00
Barium Sulphate-Vinyl Sheet, 1 psf	1.20–1.50
Vibration Damping	.25–6.00
Lead-Vinyl with 1" Foam	2.70–4.00
1" Acoustical Foam	1.00
1" Foam with Adhesive	1.25–1.50
1" Foam with 1 Mil Plastic Facing	1.25–1.50
Spray-On Ceiling Material, 1"	.35–1.00
¼" Plywood	.25
¾" Plywood	.45
18 GA Cold Rolled Steel	.30–.35
24 GA Cold Rolled Steel	.15–.20
¼" Plexiglas	2.50
¼" Lexan	4.75

PRODUCTION COSTS

One estimate[5] indicated that machine enclosures may result in productivity penalties of up to 25 percent; however, any potential adverse production influences will be dependent upon the operation involved and the enclosure design. In many cases no adverse production influences are reported, and in some cases, production rates may be seen to increase.

Table 10.3
Acoustical Enclosure Costs[4]

Option	Enclosure Description	Material Cost	Installation Cost	Total Cost	$/sq ft	Noise Reduction
1A	1 in. thick steel acoustical panels, no roof	$2,541	$288 2 men, 1½ days	$2,829	$12.63	10–12 dB
1B	With roof, ventilation, lighting, inlet and exhaust silencers	$3,483	$384 2 men, 2 days	$3,867	$14.37	15–25 dB
2A	4 in. thick steel acoustical panels, no roof	$2,874	$384 2 men, 2 days	$3,258	$14.54	12–14 dB
2B	With roof, ventilation, lighting, inlet and exhaust silencers	$3,926	$480 2 men, 2½ days	$4,406	$16.37	20–30 dB
3	1 lb/sq ft loaded vinyl curtain with roof, acoustic ventilation package, lighting	$1,756	$192 2 men, 1 day	$1,948	$ 6.85	6–9 dB
4	1 lb/sq ft loaded vinyl curtain with 1 in. acoustical foam and film facing, no roof	$1,424	$192 2 men, 1 day	$1,616	$ 7.21	10 dB
5	1.5 lb/sq ft quilted noise absorber/barrier, no roof	$1,284	$192 2 men, 1 day	$1,476	$ 6.59	10 dB

Since employees within personnel enclosures are generally engaged in the observation of a process or in the operation of controls, no adverse influence on production would be expected in most cases. Often isolating an employee from an unpleasant work environment (heat, dust, noise, etc.) may result in an increase in productivity. One recent study[6] reported that:

> In tests of production workers in air-conditioned space versus non-air-conditioned space, it was found that cool but stagnant atmosphere reduced output of the test group by nine per cent. Warm atmosphere with air movement reduced output by 15 per cent. Warm atmosphere with stagnant air reduced output by 23 per cent and warm air with high humidity reduced output by 28 per cent.

NOISE CONTROL ECONOMIC BENEFITS

An industry will generally achieve direct economic benefits from any significant reduction in workplace noise levels, whether by means of acoustical enclosures or other measures. These potential benefits may include:

REDUCED PROBABILITY OF HEARING LOSS

It has been recognized for many years that prolonged exposure to excessive noise may lead to a loss of hearing. The percentage of population expected to exhibit a permanent hearing loss due to exposure to various noise levels is presented in Table 10.4.[3] The economic consequence to an industry for the hearing loss of its employees is the payment of Workers Compensation claims. Both the total number of claims filed by employees, and the dollar value of compensation awards have shown sharp upward trends within the last two years. For estimation of potential liability due to hearing loss, an average payment of $2000 may be assumed; however, it should be recognized that in some states, hearing loss awards have exceeded $30,000 for a single individual.

Table 10.4

Percent of population exhibiting more than 25 dB hearing level re ISO ZERO after 40 years of exposure to specified noise level[3]

Noise Level	Total %	% Due to Noise	% Due to Other
80	24	0	24
85	32	8	24
90	42	18	24
95	52	28	24
100	64	40	24
105	78	54	24
110	88	64	24
115	94	70	24

Note: ISO ZERO is defined as the hearing threshold for audiometric testing by the International Standards Organization.

INCREASED PRODUCTIVITY

Reduced noise levels will generally result in a direct increase in productivity where noise is found to interfere with auditory signals related to a work function or adversely influence performance of mental or motor tasks. Increases in production outputs may also be realized due to an improvement in worker morale and attitudes as a result of noise reduction and other environmental improvements.

REDUCED ABSENTEEISM

Unscheduled absences amount to 1.5% of the potential available manpower in the United States.[7] The increase in overall absenteeism among workers in noisy areas is on the order of 1.23 workers per hundred per day. This represents an average annual direct wage cost of $115 (assuming a $4.50/hour rate) per employee, with additional costs related to fringe benefits, overtime pay for replacement workers, and poor quality or reduced production rates because of absences to key personnel.

A five-year study by Cohen[8] showed a frequency of occurrence of discrete absences to range from 30.3 for a work group exposed to noise levels above 95 dBA, to a rate of 4.2 for a similar group exposed to noise levels below 80 dBA. Another study by Raytheon showed that an absentee rate in one industry was reduced from 43% to 12% after implementation of a hearing conservation program.

REDUCED ACCIDENTS

Several recent studies have indicated a decrease in accident rates for employees in quiet work environments. The results of three studies are summarized below:[2]

| | Accident Rate | |
Investigator	High Noise	Low Noise
Cohen	9%	0.4%
NIOSH	35%	5%
Raytheon	16%	10%

Caution should be used in drawing definitive conclusions from this data (and also the absenteeism data previously presented) since the types of jobs in the noisy and quieter areas cannot be equated in all studies. However, these results may be interpreted to indicate a general trend of reduced accident rates with quieter environments.

REDUCED GOVERNMENTAL CITATIONS, PENALTIES, AND LEGAL FEES

Enforcement of the OSHA noise standard resulted in 4.5% citations due to 10,641 noise inspections between January 1973 and March 1976. While the Occupational Safety and Health Act provides for penalties up to $10,000, often no penalty or a maximum of only a few hundred dollars is assessed for noise violation, with an average penalty of approximately $40. Thus, the economic disincentive associated with an OSHA citation is not the citation fine, but in-house costs related to complying with, or contesting a noise citation. Contesting an OSHA citation may typically cost between $5000 to $20,000 in legal and consultant's fees and time requirements for plant executives and engineers. Costs associated with involved trials and higher court appeals may easily exceed $50,000. Where citations are not contested, accelerated abatement schedules may also lead to extensive costs.

ENERGY CONSUMPTION

Acoustical enclosures may result in either an energy savings or an increased energy consumption, depending upon the specific application. Due to the energy crisis and subsequent increases in power costs, energy considerations are becoming a major consideration in all engineering designs. In 1977, electrical utility costs ranged from two cents per kwh in some areas of the southeast United States up to nine cents per kwh in areas of New York. Many persons anticipate that utility costs may double within the next three years or triple within the next ten years.

Machine enclosures will result in an increased energy consumption when heat build-up decreases machine efficiency, or when machine loading is increased to provide additional cooling to compensate for an enclosure's thermal isolation.

Energy will be consumed when blowers are required for machine enclosure cooling. Typically, one air change per minute is required. Thus, ventilation of a 10 foot by 10 foot by 10 foot enclosure would require a 1000 cfm fan. A 1000 cfm fan would typically be powered by a ¼ hp fan, which would cost $0.14 per hour with a $0.03 kwh utility rate.

Employee enclosures will require energy to ventilate or cool the interior workspace. A 10 foot by 10 foot by 10 foot enclosure would typically require a 5000 BTU air-conditioner. With a $0.04 kwh utility rate, the operational cost would be $.06 per hour.

HOW ENCLOSURES CAN SAVE ENERGY

Acoustical enclosures may result in significant energy consumption reductions when the designer takes advantage of their thermal insulation or spatial isolation properties, and analyzes heat recovery applications. For example, if the heat gain from enclosed equipment can be used in an area requiring heat, energy will be saved. Energy may also be saved if the heat from an enclosed machine is ducted outside an air-conditioned work area, reducing cooling requirements for the work environment.

Two equations may be used to estimate make-up air heating costs on an hourly and yearly basis. Since there is an allowance for the efficiency of the make-up air unit, these equations will tend to give a low result if air is allowed to enter by infiltration only.

$$\text{Hourly cost} = \frac{0.001 \ QN}{q} \times c \qquad (10\text{-}4)$$

$$\text{Yearly cost} = \frac{0.154 \ QD \ dg}{q} \times c \qquad (10\text{-}5)$$

where:
- Q = air volume, cfm
- N = required heat, BTU/hr/1000 cfm (Table 10.5)
- D = operating time, hours/week
- q = available heat per unit of fuel (Table 10.6)
- dg = annual degree days (Table 10.7)
- c = cost of fuel, $/unit

EXAMPLE

Find the hourly cost of tempering 10,000 cfm of make-up air to 70 F in St. Louis, Missouri, using oil at $0.34/gallon.

Average temperature = 35 F (Figure 10.1).

$$\text{Hourly cost} = \frac{0.001 \ QN}{q} \times c = \frac{0.001 \times 10{,}000 \times 38{,}000}{106{,}500}$$

$$\times \ 0.08 = \$0.999/\text{hour}$$

EXAMPLE

Find the annual cost for the same city.
 Annual degree days, dg, = 6023 (Table 10.7)
 Operating time, D, = 40 hours/week

$$\text{Yearly cost} = \frac{0.154 \times 10,000 \times 40 \times 6023}{106,500}$$
$$\times \ \$0.34/\text{gallon} = \$1185.75/\text{year}$$

Table 10.5 Required heat for make-up air[9]

Average Outside Air Temperature, F	N, Required Heat BTU/hr/1000 cfm @ 70F
0	75,500
5	70,000
10	65,000
15	59,500.
20	54,000
25	48,500
30	43,000
35	38,000
40	32,500
45	27,000
50	21,500
55	16,000
60	11,000
65	5,500

Table 10.6. Fuel Data[9]

Fuel	Btu Per Unit	Efficiency %	Available Btu Per Unit q	Typical Cost
Coal	12,000 Btu/lb.	50	6,000	$70/ton
Oil	142,000 Btu/gal.	75	106,500	$0.3/gal
Gas Heat Exchanger	1,000 Btu/cu. ft.	80	800	$.0017/cu. ft.
Direct Fired		90	900	

Table 10.7. Heating degree-Day normals[10]

Annual Heating Degree-Day Normals

Air Discharge Temperature F (Base)	Albany	Boston	Chicago	Cleveland	Detroit	Minneapolis	N.Y.	Phila.	Pittsburgh	St. Louis	Wash., D.C.
80	11782	10409	10613	11343	10959	13176	9284	9652	10797	8943	8422
79	11425	10049	10277	10982	10605	12826	8937°	9300	10436	8624	8089
78	11062	9690	9940	10621	10256	12478	8596	8954	10076	8310	7764
77	10709	9342	9610	10265	9914	12135	8265	8619	9723	8003	7446
76	10356	8994	9283	9915	9581	11797	7938	8285	9379	7702	7139
75	10009	8652	8972	9570	9247	11475	7620	7959	9036	7413	6835
74	9669	8317	8656	9229	8920	11142	7308	7641	8702	7121	6538
73	9333	7990	8349	8898	8599	10816	7004	7328	8373	6839	6250
72	9007	7668	8046	8567	8291	10496	6706	7028	8050	6560	5974
71	8682	7354	7750	8248	7981	10180	6421	6728	7740	6289	5703
70	8364	7046	7468	7928	7678	9870	6146	6438	7429	6023	5438
69	8056	6749	7183	7617	7383	9567	5871	6158	7127	5767	5179
68	7750	6458	6905	7313	7100	9269	5606	5886	6833	5523	4929
67	7742	6175	6635	7016	6816	8975	5349	5618	6546	5277	4690
66	7162	5903	6373	6722	6543	8687	5101	5360	6272	5053	4455
65	6881	5633	6122	6445	6278	8410	4858	5109	5997	4822	4229
64	6607	5370	5875	6165	6020	8131	4621	4864	5734	4595	4014
63	6340	5118	5638	5897	5772	7858	4394	4628	5483	4379	3798
62	6081	4873	5399	5636	5533	7590	4176	4397	5234	4168	3588
61	5829	4634	5164	5381	5290	7339	3957	4172	5006	3963	3383
60	5586	4399	4936	5140	5054	7086	3747	3952	4769	3761	3182

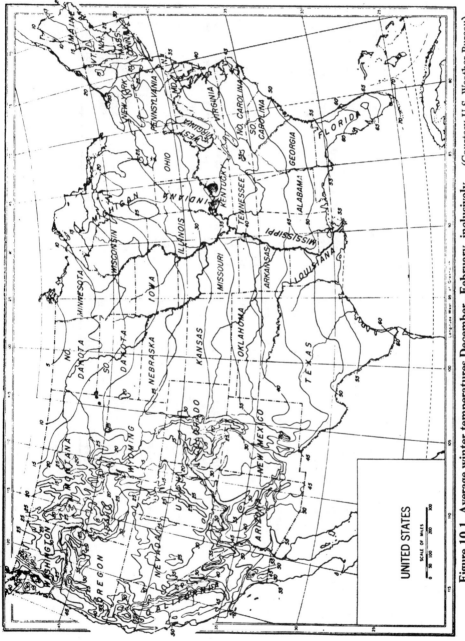

Figure 10.1. Average winter temperatures December–February, inclusively.   (Courtesy U.S. Weather Bureau)

TAX CREDITS AND
ACCELERATED DEPRECIATION

In Revenue Ruling 75-178, IRS established the policy that the classification of property as "personal" or "inherently permanent" should be made on the basis of the manner of attachment and how permanently the property is designed to remain in place. Until this ruling, a functional or equivalency test was used by IRS examiners to determine whether or not a building component was actually prefabricated. Ruling 75-178 stated:

> . . . moveable partitions that are not a permanent part of a building are tangible personal property and may qualify as "Section 38 property" for investment credit purposes.

Acoustical panels and partitions which qualify under this criterion offer two benefits:

1. These systems can be depreciated in one-third less time than permanent structures.

2. Ten percent of the price plus installation cost can be deducted directly from federal income taxes as an investment credit (subject to the dollar limitations specified in the Internal Revenue Code). It should be noted that this deduction is, in effect, a 10% rebate.

One manufacturer, American Air Filter Co., Inc., Louisville, Kentucky, offers an acoustical enclosure system which is claimed to qualify under Ruling 75-178, due to a patented joining system.

THE DESIGNER'S CHOICE

From the discussions of economic considerations in this chapter and the engineering elements in the previous chapters, it is seen that the installation of acoustical enclosures may have either extreme adverse or significant positive influences on a plant's operations.

A poorly designed acoustical enclosure may:

1. Provide only minimal noise reduction.

2. Restrict employee-machine interaction, resulting in decreased production efficiency.

3. Cause a safety hazard.

4. Increase energy consumption.

5. Be excessively costly, both in terms of initial and operational costs.

A well-designed acoustical enclosure may:

1. Provide significant noise reduction (up to 20-40 dBA).

2. Increase productivity by improving operational efficiency.

3. Improve employee efficiency by minimizing physiological distractions and increasing auditory perception.

4. Improve employee morale by providing a more pleasing work environment.

5. Protect worker safety and health.

6. Conserve energy.

7. Have only minimal initial costs.

8. Reduce operational costs.

The variables listed above are generally active variables in any noise reduction project, and the overall positive or negative impact is not established until the design is finalized. By combining the application of correct engineering principles and ingenuity, the design engineer can insure that an acoustical enclosure will have favorable cost/effectiveness and cost/benefit ratios rather than cause a production headache.

REFERENCES

1. The Bureau of National Affairs, Inc., "Noise Regulation Reporter," Number 60, 30 August 1976, p. 14.

2. Miller, R. K., *Handbook of Industrial Noise Management,* The Fairmont Press, Inc., 1976.
3. Bolt, Beranek & Newman, Inc., "Impact of Noise Control at the Workplace," Report No. 2671, October 29, 1973.
4. Stahovic, S. J. and Stone, E. W., "The Use of Absorber/ Barrier Materials for Noise Control Enclosures," *Sound and Vibration,* V. 10, n. 9, September 1976, p. 20.
5. Yerges, L. F., "Methods of Noise Control for Machinery Already Installed," *Proceedings of NOISEXPO,* September 1973, pp. 157-159.
6. "Plant Engineering Directory & Specifications Catalog," Volume 11, 1976.
7. Gatts, R. R., Massey, R. G., and Robertson, J. C., "Energy Conservation Program Guide for Industry and Commerce," *National Bureau of Standards Handbook 115,* 1974.
8. Cohen, A., "Extra-Auditory Effects of Occupational Noise: Effects on Work Performance," *National Safety News,* September 1973, pp. 68-76.
9. *Industrial Ventilation,* American Conference of Governmental Industrial Hygienists, 1976.
10. *Heating, Ventilating, and Air Conditioning Guide,* American Society of Heating, Air Conditioning, and Refrigerating Engineers, 1963.

11

Commercially Available Acoustical Enclosures and Barriers

In the United States, there are several thousand businesses engaged in the manufacturing or supply of acoustical and vibration control systems and materials. Table 11.1 presents many of the larger manufacturers of noise control enclosure and barrier systems and materials. Published literature may be obtained from these manufacturers relating to:

- Product information
- Performance test data
- Suggestions for applications
- Case histories
- General technical information
- Cost information

Figures 11.1 through 11.22 present typical applications of commercially available enclosure and barrier systems. Some of the enclosures are supplied as stock items, or fabricated from standard panels. Other units are fabricated for special applications.

Table 11.1

Company	Acoustical Panels	Seals & Gaskets	Pipe Lagging	Architectural Partitions	Engine Test Cells	Windows	Doors	Office Equipment Enclosures	Telephone Booth Enclosures	Construction Vehicle Enclosures	Audiometric Booths	FDA Information	Fire Code Information	Transparent Strip Curtains	Flexible Curtains	Modular Office Partitions	Ceilings	Machine Enclosures	Office Enclosures
ACON, INC. P.O. Box 1324, Dayton, Ohio 45401 513-276-2111			•																
ACOUSTICS INCORP., 1112 Westminster Ave., Alhambra, California 91803 213-289-0186																•			
CONSOLIDATED KINETICS CORP., 249 Fornof Lane, Col., Ohio 43207 614-443-7621												•	•	•					
CONWED, OFFICE SPACE CONTROL PRODUCTS, 2200 Highcrest Rd., St. Paul, Minn. 55113 612-645-6699	•			•	•	•	•				•	•		•		•		•	•
COUSTI-PRODUCTS, FERRO COMPOSITES, 34 Smith St., Norwalk, Conn. 06852 203-853-2123	•			•		•	•		•			•						•	•
COWL INDUSTRIES LIMITED, 44 Chauncey Ave., Toronto 18, Ontario 416-239-3988	•			•		•	•					•					•	•	•

/more/

Table 11.1 continued

Company	Office Enclosures	Machine Enclosures	Ceilings	Modular Office Partitions	Flexible Curtains	Transparent Strip Curtains	Fire Code Information	FDA Information	Audiometric Booths	Construction Vehicle Enclosures	Telephone Booth Enclosures	Office Equipment Enclosures	Doors	Windows	Engine Test Cells	Architectural Partitions	Pipe Lagging	Seals & Gaskets	Acoustical Panels
DOUG BIRON ASSOC., P.O. Box 413, Buford, GA. 30518 404-945-2929					•	•								•					•
ECKEL INDUSTRIES, INC., 155 Fawcett St., Cambridge, Mass. 617-491-3221 Morrisburg, Ontario, Canada 613-543-2967		•	•			•				•				•					•
GATES ACOUSTINET, INC., P.O. Box 1406, Santa Rosa, California 95403 707-544-2711																			
GEORGE KOGH SONS, INC., Thermal Products Div., Evansville, Ind. 47744 812-425-7321											•			•	•				•
INDUSTRIAL ACOUSTICS CO., 380 Southern Boulevard, Bronx, N.Y. 10454 212-292-0180		•	•							•	•	•		•	•				
INDUSTRIAL NOISE CONTROL, INC., 785 Industrial Dr. Elmhurst, Ill. 60126 312-834-2000		•	•							•				•	•				

INSUL-COUSTIC/BIRMA CORP., Jernee Mill, Sayreville, N.J. 08872 201-257-6674

KOPPERS CO., INC., Metal Products Div., Sound Control Dept., P.O. Box 298, Baltimore, MD. 21203 301-727-2500

KORFUND DYNAMICS CORP., Cantiague Rd., Westbury, Long Island, N.Y. 11590 516-333-7580

(LORD) ALLFORCE ACOUSTICS/LORD CORP., Erie, PA. 16512 800-458-0441

NATIONAL CELLULOSE CORP., 12315 Robin Blvd., Houston, Texas 77045 713-433-6761

NORTON SEALANTS, Granville, N.Y. 12832 800-833-9693

OWENS-CORNING FIBERGLAS CORP., Architectural Products Div., Fiberglas Tower, Toledo, Ohio 43659 419-248-8101

PPG INDUSTRIES, INC., 875 Johnson Ferry Rd., N.E. Atlanta, GA. 30342 404-255-3721

PRECISION MFG., INC., Sales Office, Bureau des Ventes, -45 Elmira Place, Bonaventure, Montreal 114 P.Q., 866-2014

PRESRAY, 159 Maple Blvd., Pawling, N.Y. 12564 914-855-1220 415-321-6002

ROSE MFG. CO., 1600 Marshall Ave., S.E. Grand Rapids, Michigan 49507 616-241-2451

ROSEMOUNT PARTITIONS, INC., Airlake Industrial Park, Box D, Lakeville, Minn. 55044 612-469-4416

/more/

Table 11.1 concluded

	Office Enclosures	Machine Enclosures	Ceilings	Modular Office Partitions	Flexible Curtains	Transparent Strip Curtains	Fire Code Information	FDA Information	Audiometric Booths	Construction Vehicle Enclosures	Telephone Booth Enclosures	Office Equipment Enclosures	Doors	Windows	Engine Test Cells	Architectural Partitions	Pipe Lagging	Seals & Gaskets	Acoustical Panels
SOUNDCOAT CO., 175 Pearl St., Brooklyn, N.Y. 11201 212-858-4100					•		•												
SOUND FIGHTER SYSTEMS, P.O. Box 6601 6135 Linwood Ave., Shreveport, LA. 71106 318-868-3626					•	•	•												
VANEC, Metro Square, 2655 Villa Creek Dr., Dallas, Texas 75234 214-693-7175		•													•				
VIBRASONICS, INC., P.O. Box 141, Carthage, Texas 75633 214-693-7175	•	•											•	•					•

Figure 11.1

A machine enclosure constructed of a unique clear barrier system that provides transmission loss as well as sound absorption. *(Courtesy of Body Guard, Inc.)*

Figure 11.2

A clear angular plexiglas barrier which focuses on sound absorbing foam and is FDA approved for bottling operations. *(Courtesy of Body Guard, Inc.)*

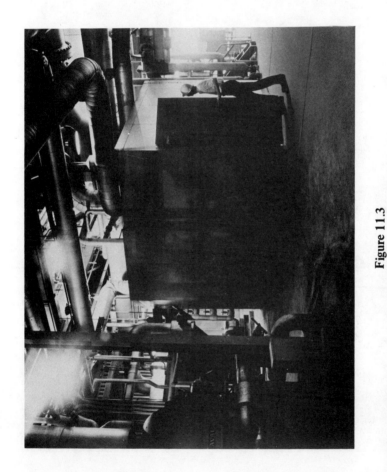

Figure 11.3

A machine enclosure for a boiler feed pump constructed with 4½" thick panels that are filled with incombustible acoustical-thermal insulating material. *(Courtesy of Environmental Elements Corp.)*

Figure 11.4
Tubular framing and leaded vinyl-absorbent foam curtain for pump,
which achieved an 18 dBA reduction. Two men installed the enclosure in
45 minutes. *(Courtesy of Singer Partitions, Inc., Chicago, IL)*

Figure 11.5

Acoustical panels to reduce sound levels in "shake-out" area. The enclosure features limp, lead-vinyl, ¾ lb curtains. Each 12'10" by 10'. Curtain panel is suspended from overhead "swing-away" track which allows easy entry of forklift trucks into shake-out areas. Acoustical panels are used on three sides to complete the enclosure. With both units operating, the acoustical panels reduced the sound level from 116 to 106 decibels; with curtains closed, the level was further reduced to 98 decibels. *(Courtesy of Singer Partitions, Inc., Chicago, IL)*

Figure 11.6
Acoustical enclosure for Davenport automatic screw machine, providing
accessibility and attenuation to below 90 dBA. *(Courtesy of Keene Corp.,*
Porta-Fab Division, St. Lous, MO)

Figure 11.7
Acoustical enclosure for automatic coil fed punch press.
(Courtesy of Allforce Acoustics, Lord Corporation, Erie, PA)

Figure 11.8
Fiberglas reinforced leaded vinyl enclosure on angle iron frame for refiner in paper mill. *(Courtesy of Brenton Industries, Inc., Amsterdam, NY)*

Figure 11.9
Rigid steel Header enclosure for National 3/16 High Speed Header. Steel tube frame, 16 gauge sheet metal panels with Quil/Teez material. Maximum noise level when completely closed 85 dBA at tooling position. *(Courtesy of Frelun Engineering Co., Rockford, IL)*

Figure 11.10

Pre-assembled acoustical enclosure (48" x 152" x 96" height) designed to reduce the noise from a coupled steam turbine, expander seal and gear unit to 90 dBA or less. *(Courtesy of Vibration and Noise Engineering Corporation, Dallas, TX)*

Figure 11.11

Sound barrier with sheet lead septum for printing press. *(Courtesy of ASARCO, New York, NY and Noise Control Associates, Montclair, NJ)*

Figure 11.12
Enclosure of Insul-Quilt for punch press. Noise level reduction from 9 to 14 dBA was achieved with the enclosure open at the top. *(Courtesy of Insul-Caustic Corp., Sayreville, NJ and Noise Control Associates, Montclair, NJ)*

Figure 11.13
Acoustical enclosure which reduced punch press noise from 114 dBA to
84 dBA. The enclosure is equipped with a forced ventilation system. The
acoustical material is 4" thick walls with the acoustical fill protected from
oil contamination by means of a thick plastic film. *(Courtesy of Noise
Control Products, Inc., New Hyde Park, NY)*

Figure 11.14
Zip-on insulation system for reducing piping noise. *(Courtesy of Accessible Products Company, Tempe, AZ)*

Figure 11.15

Enclosure for pump and 1500 horsepower electric motor installed at Fountain Valley, California water treatment plant. Note air inlet and exhaust silencing at end and top. *(Courtesy of General Acoustics Corporation, Los Angeles, CA)*

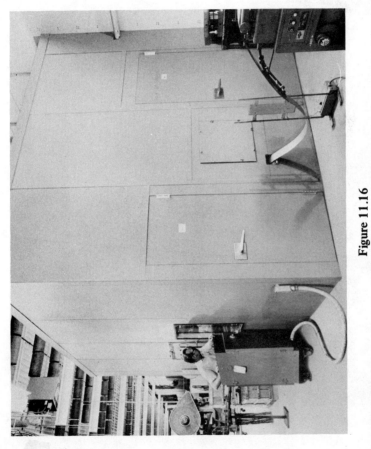

Figure 11.16

Acoustical enclosure for 100 ton, 320 stroke per minute punch press which reduced sound levels from 99 dBA to 81 dBA. *(Courtesy of Industrial Acoustics Co., Bronx, NY)*

Figure 11.17
Free hanging modular "lift off" panels suspended from a rigid steel frame-
work permit instant access to enclosed equipment with no screws, clips or
other fastening devices. *(Courtesy of Michigan Industries, Inc., Livonia,
MI)*

Figure 11.18

Acoustical enclosures may be very effective for suppressing the sound of diesels driving generators and air compressors. *(Courtesy of Farr Company, Los Angeles, CA)*

Figure 11.19
A curtain of hanging overlapping clear PVC strips that stops sound but
not visibility or traffic. *(Courtesy of Frommelt Industries, Inc., Dubuque,
Iowa)*

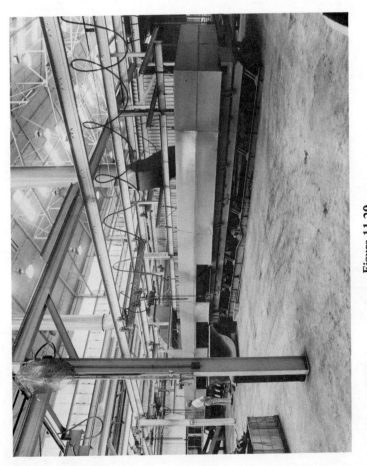

Figure 11.20

Acoustic hood for foundry conveyor and grizzly; includes ventilating fans to remove fumes. *(Courtesy of Sound Fighter Systems, Shreveport, LA)*

Figure 11.21

Modular panel enclosure featuring a sliding door system for ease of access and to accommodate space requirements. The enclosure features a unique demour table panel system so that any panel or section of the wall can be removed by undoing quarter turn quick disconnects, thus allowing easy access for repairs of the machine. *(Courtesy of Eckel Industries, Inc., Cambridge, Mass.)*

Figure 11.22

Acoustical enclosure for employees at a mining facility. *(Courtesy of Industrial Acoustics Company, Bronx, NY)*

12

Acoustical
Performance
Data

Contained in this chapter are:

1. United States Standard Gages for sheet metal (Table 12.1);

2. Sound Transmission Losses for Common Acoustical Materials (Table 12.2);

3. Sound Absorption Coefficients of General Building Materials (Table 12.3);

4. Sound Transmission Class (STC) Ratings for Common Materials (Table 12.4).

The following additional basic acoustical data is presented elsewhere in this book:

Information	Reference
Sound absorption coefficients for various thickness of glass fiber.	Figure 2.6
Sound absorption coefficients for glass fiber materials with perforated facings.	Table 3.2

| Temperature limits for acoustical materials. | Table 3.6 |
| Noise reduction for pipe coverings. | Table 7.2 |

These data provide the key to engineers for accurate sound level calculations and successful abatement programs. Using these data with the procedures presented in previous chapters should yield efficient noise control systems in all areas of industrial (noise) problems.

The sound transmission loss and absorption coefficient data presented in this chapter are designed to include most common acoustical materials. For readers desiring more extensive data, an entire book of acoustical data has been written and published by NIOSH. This publication, "Compendium of Materials for Noise Control," is designated as HEW (NIOSH) 75-165, and is available from the Superintendent of Documents, U.S. Government Printing Office, Washington, D.C. 20402.

Often in performing noise control calculations, it is necessary to convert from one set of units to another. A set of conversion tables is presented in Appendix B for this purpose.

Table 12.1. United States Standard Gages for sheet steel

Gage No.	Weight per sq ft, lbs	Approximate thickness, in.
0000000	20.00	0.490
000000	18.75	.460
00000	17.50	.429
0000	16.25	.398
000	15.00	.368
00	13.75	.337
0	12.50	.306
1	11.25	.2757
2	10.62	.2604
3	10.00	.2451
4	9.375	.2298
5	8.750	.2145
6	8.125	.1991
7	7.500	.1838
8	6.875	.1685
9	6.250	.1532
10	5.625	.1379
11	5.000	.1225
12	4.375	.1072
13	3.750	.0919
14	3.125	.0766
15	2.812	.0689
16	2.500	.0613
17	2.250	.0551
18	2.000	.0490
19	1.750	.0429
20	1.500	.0368
21	1.375	.0337
22	1.250	.0306
23	1.125	.0276
24	1.000	.0245
25	.8750	.0214
26	.7500	.0184
27	.6875	.0169
28	.6250	.0153
29	.5625	.0138
30	.5000	.0123
31	.4375	.0107
32	.4062	.0100
33	.3750	.0092
34	.3438	.0084
35	.3125	.0077
36	.2812	.0069
37	.2656	.0065
38	.2500	.0061
39	.2344	.0057
40	.2188	.0054
41	.2109	.0052
42	.2031	.0050
43	.1953	.0048
44	.1875	.0046

Table 12.2 Transmission loss of common materials

Material	lb/ sq ft	*Frequency Hz* 125	250	500	1000	2000	4000	8000
Lead								
1/32-inch thick	2	22	24	29	33	40	43	49
1/64-inch thick	1	19	20	24	27	33	39	43
Plywood								
3/4-inch thick	2	24	22	27	28	25	27	35
1/4-inch thick	0.7	17	15	20	24	28	27	25
Lead vinyl	0.5	11	12	15	20	26	32	37
Lead vinyl	1.0	15	17	21	28	33	37	43
Steel								
18-gauge	2.0	15	19	31	32	35	48	53
16-gauge	2.5	21	30	34	37	40	47	52
Sheet metal (viscoelastic								
laminate-core)	2	15	25	28	32	39	42	47
Plexiglas								
1/4-inch thick	1.45	16	17	22	28	33	35	35
1/2-inch thick	2.9	21	23	26	32	32	37	37
1-inch thick	5.8	25	28	32	32	34	46	46
Glass								
1/8-inch thick	1.5	11	17	23	25	26	27	28
1/4-inch thick	3	17	23	25	27	28	29	30
Double glass								
1/4 x 1/2 x 1/4-inch		23	24	24	27	28	30	36
1/4 x 6 x 1/4-inch		25	28	31	37	40	43	47
5/8-inch Gypsum								
On 2 x 2-inch stud		23	28	33	43	50	49	50
On staggered stud		26	35	42	52	57	55	57
Concrete, 4-inch thick	48	29	35	37	43	44	50	55
Concrete block, 6-inch	36	33	34	35	38	46	52	55
Panels of 16-gauge steel,								
4-inch absorbent,								
20-gauge steel		25	35	43	48	52	55	56

Table 12.3
Sound absorption coefficients of general building materials

Materials	Octave Band Center Frequency, Hz					
	125	250	500	1000	2000	4000
Brick, unglazed	.03	.03	.03	.04	.05	.07
Brick, unglazed, painted	.01	.01	.02	.02	.02	.03
Carpet, heavy, on concrete	.02	.06	.14	.37	.60	.65
Same, on 40 oz hairfelt or foam rubber	.08	.24	.57	.69	.71	.73
Same, with impermeable latex backing on 40 oz hairfelt or foam rubber	.08	.27	.39	.34	.48	.63
Concrete Block, coarse	.36	.44	.31	.29	.39	.25
Concrete Block, painted	.10	.05	.06	.07	.09	.08
Floors						
Concrete or terrazzo	.01	.01	.015	.02	.02	.02
Asphalt, rubber, or cork tile on concrete	.02	.03	.03	.03	.03	.02
Wood	.15	.11	.10	.07	.06	.07
Glass						
Large panes of heavy plate glass	.18	.06	.04	.03	.02	.02
Ordinary window glass	.35	.25	.18	.12	.07	.04
Gypsum Board, ½" nailed to 2x4's, 16" o.c.	.29	.10	.05	.04	.07	.09
Marble or Glazed Tile	.01	.01	.01	.01	.02	.02
Plaster, gypsum or lime, smooth finish on tile or brick	.013	.015	.02	.03	.04	.05
Plaster, gypsum or lime, rough finish on lath	.14	.10	.06	.05	.04	.03
Same, with smooth finish	.14	.10	.06	.04	.04	.03
Plywood Paneling, 3/8" thick	.28	.22	.17	.09	.10	.11

Table 12.4
Summary of STC values for various materials

	Wt, psf	Thickness	Nominal STC
Cold Rolled Steel	2.0 (18 GA)	.050	30
	2.5 (16 GA)	.060	34
	3.1 (14 GA)	.075	35
Plywood	2.0	3/4	32
	1.5	1/2	28
	1.0	3/8	26
	0.7	1/4	25
Aluminum	0.9	1/16	26
	1.7	1/8	26
	3.5	1/4	31
Leaded Vinyl	.33	.035	18
	.50	.050	20
	.75	.064	22
	1.0	.100	27
	1.5	.125	28
Lead	1.0	1/64	26
	1.5	.023	28
	3.0	1/32	31
	3.0	3/64	34
Glass	1.6	1/8	28
	2.5	3/16	31
	3.2	1/4	31
	4.8	3/8	34
	6.1	1/2	35
	9.5	3/4	37
	12.6	1	38
Plexiglas	1.5	1/4	27
	2.9	1/2	30
	5.8	1	32
Laminated glass	3.5	1/4	34
	6.0	3/8	36
	6.5	1/2	38
	9.7	5/8	40
	10.2	3/4	43

Appendix A

Basic Noise Control

Terminology

(COURTESY OF QUIETFLO, NANUET, NEW YORK)

Acoustics	The science of sound. Characteristics associated with sound, e.g., acoustic insulation. Conditions in a defined area, e.g. workshop, hall, factory, room, theater, etc. related to sound.
Absorbent:	Material of a porous nature such as mineral or glass fiber or open cell foam which has a high coefficient of absorption over an extended range of frequencies. At low frequencies the absorption increases with the thickness of the material. Used in silencers, screens, enclosures, etc.
Absorption Coefficient	The sound absorption coefficient represents the ratio of the sound absorbed to the sound incident on any material, and varies from 0 to 1.
Ambient Noise	The background or general noise existing in an area other than the source of interest.
Amplitude	Pressure variation about mean.
Attenuation	A measure of how much a sound wave will be reduced as it travels through a material (e.g., a silencer) measured in dB.
Characteristic Frequency (Natural Frequency)	Applies to everything which can vibrate, i.e., anything having elasticity and mass has a characteristic frequency or frequencies, e.g., tuning fork, Helmholtz resonator.
Decibel or dB (1/10th of a Bell)	A term borrowed from electrical sources. Because of the wide dynamic range of the human ear, pin drop to, for example, jet aircraft, the number range to measure this would be very high; therefore, the logarithmic ratio is used such that the dynamic range of

the ear is contained within the range 0–130 dB, 0 being the threshold of hearing. The reference quantity which must be stated when decibel readings are used is 2×10^{-5} Newtons per square meter (N/m^2) N.B. 1 Newton = 0.22481 lb force and $1 N/m^2$ = 0.000145 p.s.i.

dBA (a Scale) Noise readings taken with a noise level meter incorporating an A filter or weighting system—this system reduces the immediate response to low and very high frequency levels thus approximating the response of the human ear. Most current and proposed legislation are now given in dBA units.

Frequency The number of oscillations (sound) per second expressed as Hertz (Hz). 1 cycle per second = 1 Hz. Known as pitch in music.

Free Field Conditions in an area where no noise reflections of any note arise; e.g., an open field with clear unobstructed boundaries.

Fundamental Frequency The frequency with which a periodic action repeats itself. Machine (blade passing) frequency. The dominant frequency produced by machines where a periodic factor arises in manufacturing design; e.g., Roots blowers, rotary fans—gears—compressors, etc.

Harmonic Noise, with a number of components (pure tone), whose frequencies are whole numbered multiples of the base or fundamental frequency, if a component has a frequency twice that of the base it is termed second harmonic in acoustics.

Helmholtz Resonator	A resonant device for absorbing sound energy by friction in an orifice or orifices at the neck of a hollow vessel.
Hertz (Hz)	See under Frequency.
Impact Sound	Sound of transient nature caused by rapidly fluctuating forces, e.g. a drop hammer, packing machines, internal combustion engine.
Insertion Loss	The difference between the sound pressure level at one point in space before and after a silencer is attached to the noise source.
Level	Value of a quantity expressed in decibels relative to a reference value.
Loudness	The estimate of the *intensity* of a sound as measured by the human ear. It is dependent on sound pressure and frequency. The unit of loudness is the Sone.
Loudness Level	The subjective measurement of the relative *strength* of a sound by the human ear compared with a tone at 1,000 Hz. The unit is the phon. The subjective loudness level of 40 phons corresponds to a loudness of 1 Sone.
Noise Rating (NR) Curves	Curves relating sound levels in the octave bands to the center frequency of the octave bands, each given a number which is numerically equal to the sound pressure level at the intersection at 1,000 Hz—used to define acceptability of sound under various conditions and for specifying levels— now being superceded by the dBA for most purposes.
Octave	Ratio between two measured frequencies, one being twice the frequency of the other.

Octave Band	Frequency range of a noise measurement usually designated by the geometric center frequency, e.g. 500 Hz, 1KHz, etc.
Perceived Noise Level (PNdB)	Measured by the sound pressure level of a similar noise which is judged by normal individuals as being equally noisy. Used for rating aircraft noise. This similar reference noise consists of random noise between one-third of an octave and one octave wide at 1,000 Hz.
Phon	See Loudness Level.
Presbyacusis	Loss of hearing through age increase.
Pure Tone	Sound with a sinusoidal waveform— (a single note) with no harmonics.
Random Noise	A conglomeration of sounds.
Resonance	Vibration of a system caused by a certain frequency—if the amplitude falls when raising or lowering the frequency of the source, the system is in resonance.
Resonant Frequency	The frequency causing maximum amplitude.
Reverberation	Sound which builds up from various reflections on surrounding surfaces— keeps on after sound has stopped.
Reverberation Time	Time it takes for sound level to decay by 60 dB when noise stops. May vary with frequency.
Sone	See Loudness.
Sound Power	The total power of the sound radiated from a sound source. Expressed in watts.
Sound Power Level (SWL or PWL)	The total energy emitted by the source as sound—expressed in decibels—the Internationally agreed reference power is 10^{-12} Watts. (Some

	American literature uses a reference power of 10^{-13} Watts.)
Sound Pressure Level	Expressed in decibels and measured by sound meters (see also Decibel).
Transmission Loss	Normally used with reference to partitions (example a wall). It is a measure of the difference between the sound pressure level of an airborne wave incident on one side of the partitions, and the airborne wave that is transmitted by the "far" side of the partition.
Wave Length	Distance between peaks of a sine-wave —equal to the speed of sound divided by the frequency.
Weighted Sound Level	Sound level measured by a sound level meter having inbuilt filters that are more responsive to some frequencies than others, i.e., the A, B and C scales.
White Sound	Sound of a completely random nature having no dominant tone or accumulation of tones.

Appendix B

Conversion Factors

(COURTESY OF THE PURDUE ENGINEER)

MULTIPLY	BY	TO OBTAIN
abamperes	10	amperes
abamperes	3×10^{10}	statamperes
abamperes per sq cm	64.52	amperes per sq inch
abampere-turns	10	ampere-turns
abampere-turns	12.57	gilberts
abampere-turns per cm	25.40	ampere-turns per inch
abcoulombs	10	coulombs
abcoulombs	3×10^{10}	statcoulombs
abcoulombs per sq cm	64.52	coulombs per sq inch
abfarads	10^9	farads
abfarads	10^{15}	microfarads
abfarads	9×10^{20}	statfarads
abhenries	10^{-9}	henries
abhenries	10^{-6}	millihenries
abhenries	$1/9\times10^{-20}$	stathenries
abmhos per cm cube	1.662×10^2	mhos per mil foot
abmhos per cm cube	10^3	megmhos per cm cube
abohms	10^{-15}	megohms
abohms	10^{-3}	microhms
abohms	10^{-9}	ohms
abohms	$1/9\times10^{-20}$	statohms
abohms per cm cube	10^{-3}	microhms per cm cube
abohms per cm cube	6.015×10^{-3}	ohms per mil foot
abvolts	$1/3\times10^{-10}$	statvolts
abvolts	10^{-8}	volts
acres	43,560	square feet
acres	4047	square meters
acres	1.562×10^{-8}	square miles
acres	5645.38	square varas
acres	4840	square yards
acre-feet	43,560	cubic feet
acre-feet	3.259×10^5	gallons
amperes	1/10	abamperes
amperes	3×10^9	statamperes
amperes per sq cm	6.452	amperes per sq inch
amperes per sq inch	0.01550	abamperes per sq cm
amperes per sq inch	0.1550	amperes per sq cm
amperes per sq inch	4.650×10^8	statamperes per sq cm
ampere-turns	1/10	abampere-turns
ampere-turns	1.257	gilberts
ampere-turns per cm	2.540	ampere-turns per in.
ampere-turns per inch	0.03937	abampere-turns per cm
ampere-turns per inch	0.3937	ampere-turns per cm
ampere-turns per inch	0.4950	gilberts per cm
areas	0.02471	acres
areas	100	square meters
atmospheres	76.0	cms of mercury
atmospheres	29.92	inches of mercury
atmospheres	33.90	feet of water

MULTIPLY	BY	TO OBTAIN
atmospheres	10.333	kgs per sq meter
atmospheres	14.70	pounds per sq inch
atmospheres	1.058	tons per sq foot
bars	9.870×10^{-1}	atmospheres
bars	1	dynes per sq cm
bars	0.01020	kgs per square meter
bars	2.089×10^{-8}	pounds per sq foot
bars	1.450×10^{-5}	pounds per sq inch
board-feet	144 sq in. x 1 in.	cubic inches
British thermal units	0.2530	kilogram-calories
British thermal units	777.5	foot-pounds
British thermal units	1054	horsepower-hours
British thermal units	107.5	joules
British thermal units	3.827×10^{-4}	kilogram-meters
British thermal units	2.928×10^{-4}	kilowatt-hours
Btu per min	12.96	foot-pounds per sec
Btu per min	0.2356	horsepower
Btu per min	0.01757	kilowatts
Btu per min	17.57	watts
Btu per sq ft per min	0.1220	watts per square inch
bushels	1.244	cubic feet
bushels	2150	cubic inches
bushels	0.03524	cubic meters
bushels	4	pecks
bushels	64	pints (dry)
bushels	32	quarts (dry)
centares	1	square meters
centigrams	0.01	grams
centiliters	0.01	liters
centimeters	0.3937	inches
centimeters	0.01	meters
centimeters	393.7	mils
centimeters	10	millimeters
centimeter-dynes	1.020×10^{-3}	centimeter-grams
centimeter-dynes	1.020×10^{-8}	meter-kilograms
centimeter-dynes	7.376×10^{-9}	pound feet
centimeter-grams	980.7	centimeter-dynes
centimeter-grams	10^{-5}	meter-kilograms
centimeter-grams	7.233×10^{-5}	pound-feet
centimeters of mercury	0.01316	atmospheres
centimeters of mercury	0.4461	feet of water
centimeters of mercury	136.0	kgs per square meter
centimeters of mercury	27.85	pounds per sq foot
centimeters of mercury	0.1934	pounds per sq inch
centimeters per second	1.969	feet per minute
centimeters per second	0.03281	feet per second
centimeters per second	0.036	kilometers per hour
centimeters per second	0.6	meters per minute
centimeters per second	0.02237	miles per hour

MULTIPLY	BY	TO OBTAIN
centimeters per second	3.728×10^{-4}	miles per minute
cms per sec per sec	0.03281	feet per sec per sec
cms per sec per sec	0.036	kms per hour per sec
cms per sec per sec	0.02237	miles per hour per sec
circular mils	5.067×10^{-6}	square centimeters
circular mils	7.854×10^{-7}	square inches
circular mils	0.7854	square mils
cord-feet	4 ft x 4 ft x 1 ft	cubic feet
cords	3 ft x 4 ft x 4 ft	cubic feet
coulombs.	1/10	abcoulombs
coulombs.	3×10^9	statcoulombs
coulombs per sq inch	0.01550	abcoulombs per sq cm
coulombs per sq inch	0.1550	coulombs per sq cm
coulombs per sq inch	4.650×10^8	statcouls per sq cm
cubic centimeters	3.531×10^{-5}	cubic feet
cubic centimeters	6.102×10^{-2}	cubic inches
cubic centimeters	10^{-6}	cubic meters
cubic centimeters	1.308×10^{-6}	cubic yards
cubic centimeters	2.642×10^{-4}	gallons
cubic centimeters	10^{-3}	liters
cubic centimeters	2.113×10^{-8}	pints (liq)
cubic centimeters	1.057×10^{-8}	quarts (liq)
cubic feet	2.832×10^4	cubic cms
cubic feet	1728	cubic inches
cubic feet	0.02832	cubic meters
cubic feet	0.03704	cubic yards
cubic feet	7.481	gallons
cubic feet	28.32	liters
cubic feet	59.84	pints (liq)
cubic feet	29.92	quarts (liq)
cubic feet per minute.	472.0	cubic cms per sec
cubic feet per minute.	0.1247	gallons per sec
cubic feet per minute.	0.4720	liters per second
cubic feet per minute.	62.4	lbs of water per min
cubic inches	16.39	cubic centimeters
cubic inches	5.787×10^{-4}	cubic feet
cubic inches	1.639×10^{-5}	cubic meters
cubic inches	2.143×10^{-5}	cubic yards
cubic inches	4.329×10^{-3}	gallons
cubic inches	1.639×10^{-2}	liters
cubic inches	0.03463	pints (liq)
cubic inches	0.01732	quarts (liq)
cubic meters.	10^6	cubic centimeters
cubic meters.	35.31	cubic feet
cubic meters.	61,023	cubic inches
cubic meters.	1.308	cubic yards
cubic meters.	264.2	gallons
cubic meters.	10^9	liters

MULTIPLY	BY	TO OBTAIN
cubic meters	2113	pints (liq)
cubic meters	1057	quarts (liq)
cubic yards	7.646×10^5	cubic centimeters
cubic yards	27	cubic feet
cubic yards	46,656	cubic inches
cubic yards	0.7646	cubic meters
cubic yards	202.0	gallons
cubic yards	764.6	liters
cubic yards	1616	pints (liq)
cubic yards	807.9	quarts (liq)
cubic yards per minute	0.45	cubic feet per second
cubic yards per minute	3.367	gallons per second
cubic yards per minute	12.74	liters per second
days	24	hours
days	1440	minutes
days	86,400	seconds
decigrams	0.1	grams
deciliters	0.1	liters
decimeters	0.1	meters
degrees (angle)	60	minutes
degrees (angle)	0.01745	radians
degrees (angle)	3600	seconds
degrees per second	0.01745	radians per second
degrees per second	0.1667	revolutions per min
degrees per second	0.002778	revolutions per sec
dekagrams	10	grams
dekaliters	10	liters
dekameters	10	meters
dollars (U.S.)	5.182	francs (French)
dollars (U.S.)	4.20	marks (German)
dollars (U.S.)	0.2055	pounds sterling (Brit)
dollars (U.S.)	4.11	shillings (British)
drams	1.772	grams
drams	0.0625	ounces
dynes	1.020×10^{-3}	grams
dynes	7.233×10^{-5}	poundals
dynes	2.248×10^{-6}	pounds
dynes per square cm	1	bars
ergs	9.486×10^{-11}	British thermal units
ergs	1	dyne-centimeters
ergs	7.376×10^{-8}	foot-pounds
ergs	1.020×10^{-3}	gram-centimeters
ergs	10^{-7}	joules
ergs	2.390×10^{-11}	kilogram-calories
ergs	1.020×10^{-8}	kilogram-meters
ergs per second	5.692×10^{-9}	Btu per minute
ergs per second	4.426×10^{-6}	foot-pounds per min
ergs per second	7.376×10^{-8}	foot-pounds per sec

MULTIPLY	BY	TO OBTAIN
ergs per second	1.341×10^{-10}	horsepower
ergs per second	1.434×10^{-9}	kg-calories per min
ergs per second	10^{-10}	kilowatts
farads	10^{-9}	abfarads
farads	10^{-6}	microfarads
farads	9×10^{-11}	statfarads
fathoms	6	feet
feet	30.48	centimeters
feet	12	inches
feet	0.3048	meters
feet	.36	varas
feet	1/3	yards
feet of water	0.02950	atmospheres
feet of water	0.8826	inches of mercury
feet of water	304.8	kgs per square meter
feet of water	62.43	pounds per sq ft
feet of water	0.4335	pounds per sq inch
feet per minute	0.5080	centimeters per sec
feet per minute	0.01667	feet per sec
feet per minute	0.01829	kilometers per hour
feet per minute	0.3048	meters per minute
feet per minute	0.01136	miles per hour
feet per second	30.48	centimeters per sec
feet per second	1.097	kilometers per hour
feet per second	0.5921	knots per hour
feet per second	18.29	meters per minute
feet per second	0.6818	miles per hour
feet per second	0.01136	miles per minute
feet per 100 feet	1	per cent grade
feet per sec per sec	30.48	cms per sec per sec
feet per sec per sec	1.097	kms per hr per sec
feet per sec per sec	0.3048	meters per sec per sec
feet per sec per sec	0.6818	miles per hr per sec
foot-pounds	1.286×10^{-3}	British thermal units
foot-pounds	1.356×10^{7}	ergs
foot-pounds	5.050×10^{-7}	horsepower-hours
foot-pounds	1.356	joules
foot-pounds	3.241×10^{-4}	kilogram-calories
foot-pounds	0.1383	kilogram-meters
foot-pounds	3.766×10^{-7}	kilowatt-hours
foot-pounds per minute	1.286×10^{-3}	Btu per minute
foot-pounds per minute	0.01667	foot-pounds per sec
foot-pounds per minute	3.030×10^{-5}	horsepower
foot-pounds per minute	3.241×10^{-4}	kg-calories per minute
foot-pounds per minute	2.260×10^{-5}	kilowatts
foot-pounds per second	7.717×10^{-2}	Btu per minute
foot-pounds per second	1.818×10^{-3}	horsepower
foot-pounds per second	1.945×10^{-2}	kg-calories per min

MULTIPLY	BY	TO OBTAIN
foot-pounds per second	1.356×10^{-3}	kilowatts
francs (French)	0.193	dollars (U.S.)
francs (French)	0.811	marks (German)
francs (French)	0.03865	pounds sterling (Brit.)
furlongs	40	rods
gallons	3785	cubic centimeters
gallons	0.1337	cubic feet
gallons	231	cubic inches
gallons	3.785×10^{-3}	cubic meters
gallons	4.951×10^{-3}	cubic yards
gallons	3.785	liters
gallons	8	pints (liq)
gallons	4	quarts (liq)
gallons per minute	2.228×10^{-3}	cubic feet per second
gallons per minute	0.06308	liters per second
gausses	6.452	lines per square inch
gilberts	0.07958	abampere-turns
gilberts	0.7958	ampere-turns
gilberts per centimeter.	2.021	ampere-turns per inch
gills	0.1183	liters
gills	0.25	pints (liq)
grains (troy)	1	grains (av)
grains (troy)	0.06480	grams
grains (troy)	0.04167	pennyweights (troy)
grams	980.7	dynes
grams	15.43	grains (troy)
grams	10^{-3}	kilograms
grams	10^3	milligrams
grams	0.03527	ounces
grams	0.03215	ounces (troy)
grams	0.07093	poundals
grams	2.205×10^{-3}	pounds
gram-calories	3.968×10^{-3}	British thermal units
gram-centimeters	9.302×10^{-8}	British thermal units
gram-centimeters	980.7	ergs
gram-centimeters	7.233×10^{-5}	foot-pounds
gram-centimeters	9.807×10^{-5}	joules
gram-centimeters	2.344×10^{-8}	kilogram-calories
gram-centimeters	10^{-5}	kilogram-meters
grams per cc	5.600×10^{-3}	pounds per inch
grams per cc	62.43	pounds per cubic foot
grams per cc	0.03613	pounds per cubic inch
grams per cc	3.405×10^{-7}	pounds per mil-foot
hectares	2.471	acres
hectares	1.076×10^5	square feet
hectograms	100	grams
hectoliters	100	liters
hectometers	100	meters

MULTIPLY	BY	TO OBTAIN
hectowatts	100	watts
hemispheres (solid angle)	0.5	sphere
hemispheres (solid angle)	4	spherical right angles
hemispheres (solid angle)	6.283	steradians
henries	10^9	abhenries
henries	10^3	millihenries
henries	$1/9 \times 10^{-11}$	stathenries
horse-power	42.44	Btu per min
horse-power	33,000	foot-pounds per min
horse-power	550	foot-pounds per sec
horse-power	1.014	horsepower (metric)
horse-power	10.70	kg-calories per min
horse-power	0.7457	kilowatts
horse-power	745.7	watts
horse-power (boiler)	33,520	Btu per hour
horse-power (boiler)	9.804	kilowatts
horse-power-hours	2547	British thermal units
horse-power-hours	1.98×10^6	foot-pounds
horse-power-hours	2.684×10^6	joules
horse-power-hours	641.7	kilogram-calories
horse-power-hours	2.737×10^5	kilogram-meters
horse-power-hours	0.7457	kilowatt-hours
hours	60	minutes
hours	3600	seconds
inches	2.540	centimeters
inches	10^3	mils
inches	.03	varas
inches of mercury	0.03342	atmospheres
inches of mercury	1.133	feet of water
inches of mercury	345.3	kgs per square meter
inches of mercury	70.73	pounds per square ft
inches of mercury	0.4912	pounds per square in.
inches of water	0.002458	atmospheres
inches of water	0.07355	inches of mercury
inches of water	25.40	kgs per square meter
inches of water	0.5781	ounces per square in.
inches of water	5.204	pounds per square ft
inches of water	0.03613	pounds per square in.
joules	9.486×10^{-4}	British thermal units
joules	10^7	ergs
joules	0.7376	foot-pounds
joules	2.390×10^{-4}	kilogram-calories
joules	0.1020	kilogram-meters
joules	2.778×10^{-4}	watt-hours
kilograms	980,665	dynes
kilograms	10^2	grams
kilograms	70.93	poundals
kilograms	2.2046	pounds

MULTIPLY	BY	TO OBTAIN
kilograms	1.102×10^{-3}	tons (short)
kilogram-calories	3.968	British thermal units
kilogram-calories	3086	foot-pounds
kilogram-calories	1.558×10^{-2}	horsepower-hours
kilogram-calories	4183	joules
kilogram-calories	426.6	kilogram meters
kilogram-calories	1.162×10^{-3}	kilowatt-hours
kg-calories per min	51.43	foot-pounds per sec
kg-calories per min	0.09351	horsepower
kg-calories per min	0.06972	kilowatts
kgs-cms squared	2.373×10^{-3}	pounds-feet squared
kgs-cms squared	0.3417	pounds-inches squared
kilogram-meters	9.302×10^{-3}	British thermal units
kilogram-meters	9.807×10^{7}	ergs
kilogram-meters	7.233	foot-pounds
kilogram-meters	9.807	joules
kilogram-meters	2.344×10^{-3}	kilogram-calories
kilogram-meters	2.724×10^{-6}	kilowatt-hours
kgs per cubic meter	10^{-2}	grams per cubic cm
kgs per cubic meter	0.06243	pounds per cubic foot
kgs per cubic meter	3.613×10^{-5}	pounds per cubic inch
kgs per cubic meter	3.405×10^{-10}	pounds per mil foot
kgs per meter	0.6720	pounds per foot
kgs per square meter	9.678×10^{-5}	atmospheres
kgs per square meter	98.07	bars
kgs per square meter	3.281×10^{-2}	feet of water
kgs per square meter	2.896×10^{-3}	inches of mercury
kgs per square meter	0.2048	pounds per square ft
kgs per square meter	1.422×10^{-3}	pounds per square in.
kgs per sq millimeter	10^{6}	kgs per square meter
kilolines	10^{3}	maxwells
kiloliters	10^{3}	liters
kilometers	10^{5}	centimeters
kilometers	3281	feet
kilometers	10^{3}	meters
kilometers	0.6214	miles
kilometers	1093.6	yards
kilometers per hour	27.78	centimeters per sec
kilometers per hour	54.68	feet per minute
kilometers per hour	0.9113	feet per second
kilometers per hour	0.5396	knots per hour
kilometers per hour	16.67	meters per minute
kilometers per hour	0.6214	miles per hour
kms per hour per sec	27.78	cms per sec per sec
kms per hour per sec	0.9113	ft per sec per sec
kms per hour per sec	0.2778	meters per sec per sec
kms per hour per sec	0.6214	miles per hr per sec
kilometers per min	60	kilometers per hour

MULTIPLY	BY	TO OBTAIN
kilowatts	56.92	Btu per min
kilowatts	4.425×10^4	foot-pounds per min
kilowatts	737.6	foot-pounds per sec
kilowatts	1.341	horsepower
kilowatts	14.34	kg-calories per min
kilowatts	10^3	watts
kilowatt-hours	3415	British thermal units
kilowatt-hours	2.655×10^6	foot-pounds
kilowatt-hours	1.341	horsepower-hours
kilowatt-hours	3.6×10^6	joules
kilowatt-hours	860.5	kilogram-calories
kilowatt-hours	3.671×10^5	kilogram-meters
knots	6080	feet
knots	1.853	kilometers
knots	1.152	miles
knots	2027	yards
knots per hour	51.48	centimeters per sec
knots per hour	1.689	feet per sec
knots per hour	1.853	kilometers per hour
knots per hour	1.152	miles per hour
lines per square cm	1	gausses
lines per square inch	0.1550	gausses
links (engineer's)	12	inches
links (surveyor's)	7.92	inches
liters	10^3	cubic centimeters
liters	0.03531	cubic feet
liters	61.02	cubic inches
liters	10^{-3}	cubic meters
liters	1.308×10^{-3}	cubic yards
liters	0.2642	gallons
liters	2.113	pints (liq)
liters	1.057	quarts (liq)
liters per minute	5.855×10^{-4}	cubic feet per second
liters per minute	4.403×10^{-3}	gallons per second
$\log^{10} N$	2.303	$\log_e N$ or $\ln N$
$\log_e N$ or $\ln N$	0.4343	$\log^{10} N$
lumens per sq ft	1	foot-candles
marks (German)	0.238	dollars (U.S.)
marks (German)	1.233	francs (French)
marks (German)	0.04890	pounds sterling (Brit.)
maxwells	10^{-3}	kilolines
megalines	10^6	maxwells
megmhos per cm cube	10^{-3}	abmhos per cm cube
megmhos per cm cube	2.540	megmhos per in. cube
megmhos per cm cube	0.1662	mhos per mil foot
megmhos per inch cube	0.3937	megmhos per cm cube
megohms	10^6	ohms
meters	100	centimeters

MULTIPLY	BY	TO OBTAIN
meters	3.2808	feet
meters	39.37	inches
meters	10^{-3}	kilometers
meters	10^3	millimeters
meters	1.0936	yards
meter-kilograms	9.807×10^7	centimeter-dynes
meter-kilograms	10^5	centimeter-grams
meter-kilograms	7.233	pound-feet
meters per minute	1.667	centimeters per sec
meters per minute	3.281	feet per minute
meters per minute	0.05468	feet per second
meters per minute	0.06	kilometers per hour
meters per minute	0.03728	miles per hour
meters per second	1968	feet per minute
meters per second	3.284	feet per second
meters per second	3.0	kilometers per hour
meters per second	0.06	kilometers per min
meters per second	2.237	miles per hour
meters per second	0.03728	miles per minute
meters per sec per sec	3.281	feet per sec per sec
meters per sec per sec	3.6	kms per hour per sec
meters per sec per sec	2.237	miles per hour per sec
mhos per mil foot	6.015×10^{-3}	abmhos per cm cube
mhos per mil foot	6.015	megmhos per cm cube
mhos per mil foot	15.28	megmhos per in. cube
microfarads	10^{-15}	abfarads
microfarads	10^{-8}	farads
microfarads	9×10^5	statfarads
micrograms	10^{-6}	grams
microliters	10^{-6}	liters
microhms	10^3	abohms
microhms	10^{-12}	megohms
microhms	10^{-6}	ohms
microhms	$1/9 \times 10^{-17}$	statohms
microhms per cm cube	10^3	abohms per cm cube
microhms per cm cube	0.3937	microhms p in cube
microhms per cm cube	6.015	ohms per mil foot
microhms per inch cube	2.540	microhms p cm cube
microns	10^{-6}	meters
miles	1.609×10^5	centimeters
miles	5280	feet
miles	1.6093	kilometers
miles	1760	yards
miles	1900.8	varas
miles per hour	44.70	centimeters per sec
miles per hour	88	feet per minute
miles per hour	1.467	feet per second
miles per hour	1.6093	kilometers per hour

MULTIPLY	BY	TO OBTAIN
miles per hour	0.8684	knots per hour
miles per hour	26.82	meters per minute
miles per hour per sec	44.70	cms per sec per sec
miles per hour per sec	1.467	feet per sec per sec
miles per hour per sec	1.6093	kms per hour per sec
miles per hour per sec	0.4470	M per sec per sec
miles per minute	2682	centimeters per sec
miles per minute	88	feet per second
miles per minute	1.6093	kilometers per hour
miles per minute	0.8684	knots per minute
miles per minute	60	miles per hour
milligrams	10^{-2}	grams
millihenries	10^6	abhenries
millihenries	10^{-3}	henries
millihenries	$1/9 \times 10^{-14}$	stathenries
milliliters	10^{-2}	liters
millimeters	0.1	centimeters
millimeters	0.03937	inches
millimeters	39.37	mils
mils	0.002540	centimeters
mils	10^{-3}	inches
miner's inches	1.5	cubic feet per min
minutes (angle)	2.909×10^{-4}	radians
minutes (angle)	60	seconds (angle)
months	30.42	days
months	730	hours
months	43,800	minutes
months	2.628×10^6	seconds
myriagrams	10	kilograms
myriameters	10	kilowatts
myriawatts	10	kilometers
ohms	10^9	abohms
ohms	10^{-6}	megohms
ohms	10^6	microhms
ohms	$1/9 \times 10^{-11}$	statohms
ohms per mil foot	166.2	abohms per cm cube
ohms per mil foot	0.1662	abohms per cm cube
ohms per mil foot	0.06524	microhms per in. cube
ounces	8	drams
ounces	437.5	grains
ounces	28.35	grams
ounces	0.0625	pounds
ounces (fluid)	1.805	cubic inches
ounces (fluid)	0.02957	liters
ounces (troy)	480	grains (troy)
ounces (troy)	31.10	grams
ounces (troy)	20	pennyweights (troy)
ounces (troy)	0.08333	pounds (troy)

MULTIPLY	BY	TO OBTAIN
ounces per square inch	0.0625	pounds per sq inch
pennyweights (troy)	24	grains (troy)
pennyweights (troy)	1.555	grams
pennyweights (troy)	0.05	ounces (troy)
perches (masonry)	24.75	cubic feet
pints (dry)	33.60	cubic inches
pints (liquid)	28.87	cubic inches
poundals	13,826	dynes
poundals	14.10	grams
poundals	0.03108	pounds
pounds	444.823	dynes
pounds	7000	grains
pounds	453.6	grams
pounds	16	ounces
pounds	32.17	poundals
pounds (troy)	0.8229	pounds (av)
pound-feet	1.356×10^7	centimeter-dynes
pound-feet	13,825	centimeter-grams
pound-feet	0.1383	meter-kilograms
pounds-feet squared	421.3	kgs-cms squared
pounds-feet squared	144	pounds-ins squared
pounds-inches (squared)	2.926	kgs-cms squared
pounds-inches (squared)	6.945×10^{-3}	pounds-feet squared
pounds of water	0.01602	cubic feet
pounds of water	27.68	cubic inches
pounds of water	0.1198	gallons
pounds of water per min	2669×10^{-4}	cubic feet per sec
pounds per cubic foot	0.01602	grams per cubic cm
pounds per cubic foot	16.02	kgs per cubic meter
pounds per cubic foot	5.787×10^{-4}	pounds per cubic inch
pounds per cubic foot	5.456×10^{-9}	pounds per mil foot
pounds per cubic inch	27.68	grams per cubic cm
pounds per cubic inch	2.768×10^4	kgs per cubic meter
pounds per cubic inch	1728	pounds per cubic foot
pounds per cubic inch	9.425×10^{-6}	pounds per mil foot
pounds per foot	1.488	kgs per meter
pounds per inch	178.6	grams per cm
pounds per mil foot	2.306×10^6	grams per cubic cm
pounds per square foot	0.01602	feet of water
pounds per square foot	4.882	kgs per square meter
pounds per square foot	6.944×10^{-3}	pounds per sq inch
pounds per square inch	0.06804	atmospheres
pounds per square inch	2.307	feet of water
pounds per square inch	2.036	inches of mercury
pounds per square inch	703.1	kgs per square meter
pounds per square inch	144	pounds per sq foot
quadrants (angle)	90	degrees
quadrants (angle)	5400	minutes

MULTIPLY	BY	TO OBTAIN
quadrants (angle)	1.571	radians
quarts (dry)	67.20	cubic inches
quarts (liq)	57.75	cubic inches
quintals	100	pounds
quires	25	sheets
radians	57.30	degrees
radians	3438	minutes
radians	0.637	quadrants
radians per second	57.30	degrees per second
radians per second	0.1592	revolutions per second
radians per second	9.549	revolutions per min
radians per sec per sec	573.0	revs per min per min
radians per sec per sec	9.549	revs per min per sec
radians per sec per sec	0.1592	revs per sec per sec
reams	500	sheets
revolutions	360	degrees
revolutions	4	quadrants
revolutions	6.283	radians
revolutions per minute	6	degrees per second
revolutions per minute	0.1047	radians per second
revolutions per minute	0.01667	revolutions per sec
revs per min per min	1.745×10^{-3}	rads per sec per sec
revs per min per min	0.01667	revs per min per sec
revs per min per min	2.778×10^{-4}	revs per sec per sec
revolutions per second	360	degrees per second
revolutions per second	6.283	radians per second
revolutions per second	60	revs per min
revs per sec per sec	6.283	rads per sec per sec
revs per sec per sec	3600	revs per min per min
revs per sec per sec	60	revs per min per sec
rods	16.5	feet
seconds (angle)	4.848×10^{-6}	radians
spheres (solid angle)	12.57	steradians
spherical right angles	0.25	hemispheres
spherical right angles	0.125	spheres
spherical right angles	1.571	steradians
square centimeters	1.973×10^{5}	circular mils
square cnetimeters	1.076×10^{-3}	square feet
square centimeters	0.1550	square inches
square centimeters	10^{-6}	square meters
square centimeters	100	square millimeters
sq cms-cms sqd	0.02402	sq inches-inches sqd
square feet	2.296×10^{-5}	acres
square feet	929.0	square centimeters
square feet	144	square inches
square feet	0.09290	square meters
square feet	3.587×10^{-3}	square miles
square feet	.1296	square varas

MULTIPLY	BY	TO OBTAIN
square feet	1/9	square yards
sq feet-feet sqd	2.074×10^4	sq inches-inches sqd
square inches	1.273×10^6	circular mils
square inches	6.452	square centimeters
square inches	6.944×10^{-3}	square feet
square inches	10^6	square mils
square inches	645.2	square millimeters
sq inches-inches sqd	41.62	sq cms-cms sqd
sq inches-inches sqd	4.823×10^{-5}	sq ft-feet sqd
square kilometers	247.1	acres
square kilometers	10.76×10^6	square feet
square kilometers	10^6	square meters
square kilometers	0.3861	square miles
square kilometers	1.196×10^6	square yards
square meters	2.471×10^{-4}	acres
square meters	10.764	square feet
square meters	3.861×10^{-7}	square miles
square meters	1.196	square yards
square miles	640	acres
square miles	27.88×10^6	square feet
square miles	2.590	square kilometers
square miles	3,613,040.45	square varas
square miles	3.098×16^6	square yards
square millimeters	1.973×10^3	circular mils
square millimeters	0.01	square centimeters
square millimeters	1.550×10^{-3}	square inches
square mils	1.273	circular mils
square mils	6.452×10^{-6}	square centimeters
square mils	10^{-6}	square inches
square varas	.0001771	acres
square varas	7.716049	square feet
square varas	.0000002765	square miles
square varas	.857339	square yards
square yards	2.066×10^{-4}	acres
square yards	9	square feet
square yards	0.8361	square meters
square yards	3.228×10^{-7}	square miles
square yards	1.1664	square varas
statamperes	$1/3 \times 10^{-10}$	abamperes
statamperes	$1/3 \times 10^{-9}$	amperes
statcoulombs	$1/3 \times 10^{-10}$	abcoulombs
statcoulombs	$1/3 \times 10^{-9}$	coulombs
statfarads	$1/9 \times 10^{-20}$	abfarads
statfarads	$1/9 \times 10^{-11}$	farads
statfarads	$1/9 \times 10^{-5}$	microfarads
stathenries	9×10^{20}	abhenries
stathenries	9×10^{11}	henries
stathenries	9×10^{14}	millihenries

MULTIPLY	BY	TO OBTAIN
statohms	9×10^{20}	abohms
statohms	9×10^{5}	megohms
statohms	9×10^{17}	microhms
statohms	9×10^{11}	ohms
statvolts	3×10^{10}	abvolts
statvolts	300	volts
steradians	0.1592	hemispheres
steradians	0.07958	spheres
steradians	0.6366	spherical right angles
steres	10^{3}	liters
temp (degs C) +273	1	abs temp (degs C)
temp (degs C) +17.8	1.8	temp (degs Fahr)
temp (degs F) +460	1	abs temp (degs F)
temp (degs F) −32	5/9	temp (degs Cent)
tons (long)	1016	kilograms
tons (long)	2240	pounds
tons (metric)	10^{3}	kilograms
tons (metric)	2205	pounds
tons (short)	907.2	kilograms
tons (short)	2000	pounds
tons (short) per sq ft	9765	kgs per square meter
tons (short) per sq ft	13.89	pounds per sq inch
tons (short) per sq in.	1.406×10^{6}	kgs per square meter
tons (short) per sq in.	2000	pounds per sq inch
varas	2.7777	feet
varas	33.3333	inches
varas	.000526	miles
varas	.9259	yards
volts	10^{8}	abvolts
volts	1/300	statvolts
volts per inch	3.937×10^{7}	abvolts per cm
volts per inch	1.312×10^{-3}	statvolts per cm
watts	0.05692	Btu per min
watts	10^{7}	ergs per second
watts	44.26	foot-pounds per min
watts	0.7376	foot-pounds per sec
watts	1.341×10^{-3}	horsepower
watts	0.01434	kg-calories per min
watts	10^{-3}	kilowatts
watt-hours	3.415	British thermal units
watt-hours	2655	foot-pounds
watt-hours	1.341×10^{-3}	horsepower-hours
watt-hours	0.8605	kilogram-calories
watt-hours	367.1	kilogram-meters
watt-hours	10^{-3}	kilowatt-hours
webers	10^{8}	maxwells
weeks	168	hours
weeks	10,080	minutes

MULTIPLY	BY	TO OBTAIN
weeks	604,800	seconds
yards	91.44	centimeters
yards	3	feet
yards	36	inches
yards	0.9144	meters
yards	1.08	varas
years (common)	365	days
years (common)	8760	hours
years (leap)	366	days
years (leap)	8784	hours

Index